ARBROATH

S.

THE GORSE AND THE BRIAR

C C M'Evoy

ROMANY BOY

Fr.

THE GORSE AND THE BRIAR

Patrick A. McEvoy

Eight Drawings by

Christopher C. McEvoy

London ★ *1940*

READERS' UNION LIMITED

MADE 1940 IN GREAT BRITAIN
PRINTED BY MORRISON & GIBB LTD
FOR READERS' UNION LTD
CHANDOS PLACE, CHARING CROSS, LONDON, W.C.2

POSTAL AND ADMINISTRATIVE ADDRESS
DUNHAMS LANE, LETCHWORTH, HERTS

*PUBLISHED IN ASSOCIATION WITH
GEORGE G. HARRAP & CO LTD*

ILLUSTRATIONS

❧ I ❧

AT FOUR O'CLOCK ON A COLD FEBRUARY AFTERNOON IN 1934 I sat by the roadside watching a horse and trap disappearing across the downs. I listened to the soft beating of hooves, and when the figure of the driver vanished below the skyline I turned and looked down at the smoke drifting from the cottage chimneys in the village at the foot of the hill. It was Imber, one of the loneliest villages in Wiltshire, and it lay shrouded by mist in a sheltered hollow. The sun had disappeared behind the farther hills, and as I waited the sky darkened and a deep, blood-red light spread over the downs.

I stood up and presently I saw my brother, a greyhound at his heels, making his way from a farm partly hidden by tall beech-trees. Leaving a tent, a bundle of blankets, and an entanglement of pots, pans, and ropes in a heap by the roadside, I walked up the track to meet him. I knew that he would not take the trouble to shout, and tilting my head on one side I looked at him inquiringly. He made no sign, however, and his face remained expressionless. I looked at the greyhound, but she was engrossed, it seemed, in lifting her feet clear of each long blade of grass which had been left uneaten by the sheep.

We approached to within twenty yards of each other.

" Well? " I said.

7

Christopher waited until he was able to speak without raising his voice.

" The place is empty except for an old black sow," he said. " The house and most of the buildings have fallen down."

The greyhound sat on her haunches and shivered. I looked at her and promptly tucked up the collar of my overcoat.

" Is there plenty of wood? "

" Ample. There's nothing to stop us camping there to-night."

We returned to the roadside and picked up the tent, the rods, the blankets, and the pots and pans, which we had unloaded from the trap, and started up the track to the deserted farm.

" What did you give the boy for driving us here? " Christopher asked.

" I gave him ten shillings."

" Sixpence a mile."

" Ninepence a mile," I contradicted. " We gave him five pints of beer when we stopped to rest the pony at Holt and Tinhead."

On this freezing day in the middle of February we had come on to the Wiltshire Downs searching for a desolate place in which to live. The wildness of the country had attracted us to the downs above Imber. We intended to buy or rent a piece of ground, to build a rough house in wood or stone, and afterwards to work in solitude. We had settled to grow our own food and to keep a horse and trap and a tent so that we could travel whenever we grew tired of living in one place. In January we had made several journeys across Salisbury Plain and the Marlborough Downs, but on each occasion we had failed to find a spot which was in any way suitable. We had been unable to find a sheltered hollow or a clump of trees where the country was wild and unspoilt.

During the earlier part of the winter we had been living in a house in Somerset. The previous night we had slept under a roof for the last time for several years, and in the morning we had collected our rod tent (Gypsy tent), blankets, pots and pans, and loaded them in a hired trap which had brought us to the downs above Imber.

Beside the ruins of the deserted farm we selected a dry, flat piece of grass, sheltered from the prevailing wind by the beech-trees and the decayed outbuildings. I set the tent sticks in the ground, using the kettle iron as a crowbar, and threw the waterproof sheet over the framework. I then filled the bottom of the tent with dry straw, which I pulled from a rick as decayed as the farm itself, while Christopher gathered wood from the ruins and under the trees. The sky grew dark and we lit the fire in front of the tent and hung the kettle on the iron. The moon, brilliant in the frost, rose above the downs and lit the hills so that the cattle and sheep could be seen grazing on the slopes. We ate and drank and smoked in silence. The only noises which we heard were the crackle of the burning beech-wood, the bleating of the sheep, the hollow tinkle of the leaders' bells, and the cries of the peewits attracted out by the moon. The derelict farm lay in darkness except for rays of moonlight which here and there shone in through the trees and lit up the beams of a broken roof or an empty window-frame. A silence which was almost oppressive hung over the ruins. The sudden shuffle of a rat was followed by a sudden silence as if the animal was waiting for an echo of the noise which had momentarily shattered the deathlike stillness.

An owl presently alighted in the beech-trees, and when it hooted the greyhound got up from the fire and stood growling at the moonbeams and shadows among the ruins.

> The rats, the owls, the lizards crawl
> In the skilling where the calves were born,
> The rats, the owls, the lizards creep
> Where the farmer's children used to sleep.

At half-past eight, having burnt all the firewood which we had collected, we shut up the tent and made our way down to the village, the lights of which we could see two miles across the downs. The farms and cottages in Imber are built of red brick reinforced with tarred oak beams. On one side of the road is a kind of dyke or stream, spanned at intervals by wooden and stone bridges. The stream, however, was quite dry and only two wells out of twenty were in use in the village. Most of the cottages are set back about thirty yards from the road, and between the ends of their gardens and the pavement runs a wall, made of mud, rubble, lime, and straw and covered on top with a narrow thatch. In the afternoon, on our way through Imber, I saw a number of mules drawing carts and water-barrels about the village.

We went into the public-house. The bar was deserted except for the son of the blacksmith and the landlord, who was sitting over the fire looking very depressed. We ordered two pints of draught bitter.

" Can you tell me why there are so many mules in this village? " I said to the blacksmith's son while Christopher was paying for the beer. " I have never seen so many in England."

He said that about ten thousand were sold on the Plain after the War.

" Do you know of a man," said Christopher, " who would be likely to sell one? "

" No," replied the blacksmith's son. " A mule is one of the most difficult things to buy, or breed, or kill. They never, like donkeys, die a natural death, and they kick in every direction like a cow. The men about here say that they'll stand double the work of a horse of their size, but for my part I wouldn't have one for a gift."

He reminded me of an old horseman who said that the only thing he had against Christ was that he rode a mule.

We drank our beer and played darts until the oil lamp above the dart-board burnt out.

" What is the history of the old farm up on the hills? " asked Christopher, sitting down beside the fire.

" The old broken-down place up in the beech-trees? It was used as a shelling target during the War."

We discovered that Imber and the downs for six miles to the west and thirty to the east belonged to the War Office; and that every year from the spring to the autumn our future battles, if they are not won (heaven help them!) on the playing fields of Eton, will be won on these bleak downs. The blacksmith's son was working for the War

Office, and we gathered that his job included anything from locating water, digging drains, and looking for officials lost on the downs. He appeared to know every stone, every bush, every tree, and every hillock in the neighbourhood. The War Office, at least, must have been glad to discover an efficient English poacher.

In the afternoon I had noticed two immense thatched grain barns in a farmyard beside the road—they were the finest barns I have ever seen—and as I then thought that we would settle in the neighbourhood I was very disappointed to hear that two corrugated iron roofs had been ordered for them by the War Office. A new thatch would have amounted to only half the expense and would have lasted approximately fifteen years.

" One day last week," said the blacksmith's son, " a young official drew up in a car and said that he wanted me to help him measure the roofs of the barns. I pretended to know nothing about the job. He went up the ladder and I never saw a man get so tied up in my life. He called me up onto the roof, but before I had reached the top of the ladder he got the tape caught up and I had to climb down, shift the ladder, and release the tape. When at last he worked out his measurements, I told him that I thought he was ordering too much material. ' Look here,' I said, ' if you drive up to Mr ——'s place and borrow his longest ladder I'll measure the roofs and we'll compare our figures.' I had no need for the ladder, but I didn't intend to give away all I knew. I had it all measured out and on paper before he returned. All the same, he stuck to his own figures."

"The War Office intended to use this village for experimental shelling," he continued a few minutes later, "and it's only the corpses in the churchyard that have saved the village from being blown to pieces. The Church will not let them remove or damage the bodies."

After the public-house closed we talked in the road until midnight. We then said good night to the blacksmith's son and walked back to the camp. When I stirred the fire the ashes were still red, and as we warmed ourselves before going to bed we decided that, if no one attempted to move us from the derelict farm, we would walk to Warminster in the morning and look for a pony or a donkey.

The sun was shining and the air was keen when I awoke. A white frost covered the ground, and I broke an inch of ice in the water-trough in the adjoining field before I could fill the kettle. One of the most important reasons for rising early during the two days in which we camped in this spot was to reach the trough before the cows drank. We shut up the tent when we had finished our breakfast, and, after talking to a shepherd who was working in the lambing pens near the farm, we set off for Warminster. In Imber we passed a lorry unloading corrugated iron sheets outside the thatched barns. We waited for the public-house to open, and when we had each drunk a pint of beer we became more indifferent to the activities of the War Office at Imber, and we began to enjoy the seven miles' walk across the downs.

Presently we came to a steep, winding hill overlooking Warminster, and in half an hour we were in the town, starting our search for a pony. I do not think I could give a better description of Warminster than by quoting a few lines of *The Rural Rides*. I am, however, afraid that no country town in England is as pleasant to look at to-day as it was in Cobbett's time.

Warminster is a very nice town: everything belonging to it is solid and good. There are no villainous gingerbread houses running up, and no nasty, shabby-genteel people; no women trapesing about with showy gowns and dirty necks; no Jew-looking fellows with dandy coats, dirty shirts and half heels to their shoes. A really nice and good town. It is a great corn market: one of the greatest in this part of England; and here things are conducted in the good, old, honest fashion. The corn is brought and pitched in the market before it is sold; and, when sold, it is paid for on the nail; and all is over and the farmers and millers gone home by daylight.

Our clothes were ragged and faded and we had not shaved for three days. I could not make up my mind whether the people in Warminster genuinely did not intend to sell their horses, their ponies, their donkeys, or whether they were prejudiced by our appearance. We searched high and low. No one would deal with us, but every one knew of a man who kept a pony which he never used. On several occasions we walked, hopefully, right across the town in order to interview one of these promising people, only to find that their pony or donkey was lame, in foal, or working regularly for its owner. In the course of our search we made several journeys up and down the main street; we were very intent upon our errand and it was a long time before we grew aware of a peculiar disorder behind us. Ahead everything ran normally, but presently it became impossible to ignore the raised voices and screech of brakes at our heels.

Our greyhound, who was tied to a piece of rope, looked up at us and wagged her tail. Nell, as bitches go, was singularly attractive, and for a long time we had noticed that every dog who set eyes on her was seized with ecstasy. Doddering old Poms, who for months had been too weak to walk, would spring from their mistresses' arms and tear after her. Innocent young pups would fly from their perplexed mothers to lay down their lives or, had they been permitted, to follow her to the end of the world. I was almost frightened to turn round and look at the havoc which raged in the street. A feeble old lady in the distance was running, panting for breath and waving her umbrella in a frantic effort to recapture a small Pekinese. A sobbing girl dragged the mutilated corpse of a mongrel from under the wheel of a lorry, and all up the road, as far as the eye could reach, a host of dogs of all colours and sizes were seething after us—loyal sheep-dogs, who had left their flocks, pious-looking Yorkshire terriers, Bedlington terriers, Dalmatians, Pekineses, Sealyhams, lurchers, Airedales, greyhounds, bulldogs and bloodhounds, mastiffs and wolf-hounds, Newfoundlands, Alsatians, Dandie Dinmonts, Pomeranians, French poodles and Schipperkes.

At first we did not know whether to run or to walk, to turn to the left or the right. A green bus had stopped a few yards ahead and, pointing it out to Christopher, I sprang inside. No one, least of all the dogs, seemed to expect this move. I shall never forget their faces as long as I live. I have looked at a departing face with the same dejected passion. The dogs collected round the bus and gazed wistfully up at Nell, who sprang upon a seat by a window.

> Where crowned with blazing light and maiestie
> She proudly sits . . .
> So at her presence all surprised and tooken
> Await the sentence of her scornful eies:
> He whom she favours lives, the other dies.

We discovered that the bus passed within four miles of a farm where, six months before, we had hired a horse. It was a fourteen-hand cob and we decided to try and buy it, unless we heard of something smaller. We got off the bus, and at five o'clock we reached the farm. We met, however, another disappointment, for the horse, which only had one eye, had developed a cataract and had been sold at Frome market. The farmer and his wife gave us tea as soon as the milking was finished, and before we left told us of a family of Gypsies, camping in the neighbourhood, who had several ponies, a cob, a donkey, and a mule.

After a mile and a half's walk along a narrow country lane we found the Gypsies' place. It was more of a settlement than a camp, for the caravans and tents and traps stood in a yard, fenced in on one side and enclosed by a row of stables on the other. Three waggons decorated with carving and lined out with bright colours stood in one corner, and opposite them was a large tent, from the roof of which a narrow stove chimney smoked. In the middle of the yard a boy was chopping logs of wood and loading them into a four-wheel trap. He did not look up at us and we walked across the yard to an open wood fire, where a wizened old man was sitting making rabbit nets, and a younger man, with a thick, bushy moustache, was splitting briars for basket-making.

On our entering the yard a violin had been screeching up and down the scales, but as soon as the Gypsies' dogs began barking the noise stopped, and a dark little girl, violin and bow in hand, appeared at the door of a waggon. The man with the bushy moustache stopped scraping the briars and looked up, the old man put down the rabbit net, and three or four faces peered from under the canvas of the tent.

" Good afternoon," said Christopher.

" Good afternoon, young fellow," returned the younger man, glancing curiously at us.

" I heard that you have one or two ponies here," continued Christopher. " We're looking out for one."

" What do you mean ' looking out for one '? " said the man.

" I mean we are looking out for one to buy."

The man put his knife down and looked thoughtful.

" You great *dinelo* [fool], why don't you answer the young fellows? " said the wizened old man suddenly. " Can't you see they're out for a deal? "

" I can," answered the younger man as he turned to Christopher. " I'm married to naught but my woman, brother. I've got plenty of horses and I'm open to trade wi' any of 'em."

" That's the proper way to speak, Luke," said the old man approvingly. " If you'd bid and stared at me, as you did at the two young men, I'd have said, ' What is you staring at, great blood-eyes?' Sit down and have a warm, my brothers."

We seated ourselves on a couple of boxes by the fire and gave the younger man a cigarette. The old man was smoking a short clay pipe, but he accepted a cigarette, which he broke up and stuffed in his pipe.

"Tell me, young fellow, if you is travellers, where is you stopping?"

"On the Imber Downs, against the old broken-down farm," I said.

"I know where you mean, young man, agen the milestones. I've stopped up there many a time. I've picked pounds' worth of mushrooms the other side of those hills. I've— Drat the devil dogs! You can never have any peaceable conversation here!"

A sleek lurcher bitch, her bristles up, had seized hold of our greyhound with a ferocious growl, and in a moment the two dogs were fighting savagely in the middle of the yard. Over and over they rolled, their teeth gnashed together and blood ran from their mouths. The man with the black moustache jumped up, whipped off his belt, and beat the lurcher off. Nell whimpered pathetically, limped away, and took refuge under one of the waggons.

"The dog's got pups," said the man, after he had given the lurcher to a child to tie up in the tent. "*Dordi dordi!* [Dear me!] She reminds me of my woman with her *chavies* [children]. Sit down, young man. She used to be just like that bitch."

"Why was she?" I asked.

"Because she was so wild over her young one, brother.

18

She was only a girl of about eighteen when I had her, and we used to travel in Herefordshire."

He kicked the fire and made it blaze up.

" The little girl—she was a pretty black-haired *chavie*—was just beginning to run about, and one day a *bori rawnie* [big lady] in a handsome motor-car stops agen the camp. She gets out and bides talking to us for five or ten minutes. The *chavie* is running about round her feet, and she asks a main lot of questions about her. Well, presently the *rawnie* takes the little girl up in her arms, kisses her, and pulls her fur coat round her. ' I must keep this little girl ! ' she says. ' I'll give you what money you ask.' Oh, my dear God ! My wife, young man, runs at the *rawnie*, she tears the fur coat nearly off her, she takes hold of the child, she cries and she calls the woman all the dirty names she knowed. God, how she *trashed* [frightened] the *rawnie* ! If I hadn't held her she'd have ripped all the clothes off the dear woman. But, young man, you ought to have seen the lovely presents she brought to us the next day. She brought cakes, chocolate—curse the smoke, the devil must be in this fire !—fruit, suits of clothes, and a Christmas pudding. She said that my woman was the best little mother in the world, but, do you know, she'd never get out of her motor-car again."

When the man with the moustache had finished speaking, I asked him how long the little girl had been learning to play the violin.

" Not many weeks, young man," he answered. " She's at it all day long and I makes no doubt she'll learn to play it in time. Sometimes I'd like to break the thing up, but I'm afraid that she'd go cranky if I did. It's getting dark, brothers; if you want to look at any horses you'd better come now."

We left the fire and followed the man into the stables, where he showed us a fine-looking skewbald pony.

" Look at this little animal," he said. " I told you a lie when I said that I was open to trade with any of my horses. My woman would kill me stone dead if I was to sell that pony. I'm open to trot any Romany man, or any *gorgio* man, in this country, for a five-pound note."

We passed on to the next stall.

" Here's a useful pony," he went on. " She's clean and sound, but I'm afraid that I should want too much money for her."

" How much are you asking? "

" Ten pounds. I'll sell you a cheap trap and a set of harness and you can drive her back to yer place. Everything shall be fair and straightforward."

" We don't want to pay more than half the money you're asking," I said. "And we won't require a trap, as we intend to pack our tent and things on the pony's back."

" On the pony's back! " repeated the man. " In the dear God's name, tell me why you intend to do that! "

I attempted to explain that we believed it would be better for travelling about the downs, but I could not convince him and presently we went on to the next stall.

" Now this is a *gry* that'll just suit you," he said, pointing to a small black pony. " You couldn't get a better pony for your job, young man. I'll sell you that at seven pounds ten, but if you can bring me anything of yer own I'll make a chop with you."

" We've no horses of our own at present," said Christopher. " Let's have a look at her out in the daylight."

The man untied the black pony and led her out into the yard. She stood about eleven hands. After examining her feet and legs I looked at her mouth.

" Is she about four? " I asked.

" Yes, young man, she's a late foal, she's coming four this time."

" Will you take five pounds ready money? " said Christopher.

" No, young man, I couldn't take less than what I asked you."

" We couldn't possibly give you as much as that."

The man was silent for a while. " I tell you what," he said at last, " you can have the pony at seven pounds, but if you haven't got all the money I'm not afraid to trust you for a pound or a couple of pounds."

" We may never see you again," I said. " Will you take five pounds ten? "

" No, brother, I couldn't do it. Give me one of your cigarettes. Thanks."

The wizened old man seemed to be thoroughly enjoying the deal. Smoking his pipe, he watched us and cried : " Go on, Luke ! Let's see you make a deal ! Make a deal, my brothers, make a deal ! There's nothing I likes to watch more than a bit o' trade among travelling folk."

We argued for five or ten minutes, then the man with the black moustache thrust out his right hand and offered the pony to us at six pounds. Christopher struck the extended hand in the fashion of the Gypsy horse-dealer and the bargain was made. After we had paid the man with six pound-notes he went into the tent, changed one note, and gave us half a crown 'luck money.' The old man then took off his hat, and passing it round demanded the usual premium for his services in encouraging trade. The man with the moustache reluctantly put a shilling in the " old miser's " hat, we did likewise, and when the pony had been returned to its stall the three of us went back to the fire.

" I wish my old woman and I were young enough to be out travelling again," said the old man, stuffing another of our cigarettes into his pipe. " When you'm bin in one place all the time you understand what a good thing it is to be travelling, my son."

" How long have you been here? "

" Oh, a terrible long time, young man. It must be close on two years, but I seems to feel it most now when the spring's coming on. I can see you likes travelling. There's naught I used to like better than to pull up in a green lane, pitch my tent on the fresh grass, and on the light evenings watch the horses graze up and down the lane. Young man, I've called it a dog's life often enough, but then I've called me dear wife an old bitch more than once."

We sat and talked until six o'clock, when the old man suggested walking across the fields to the public-house in the village.

" It's not often that I leaves this place, but you seems two good-hearted young men and it seems to me uncivil to trade with strangers and not drink with them." He stood up and knocked his pipe out. " Luke, my son," said he, " just hand me those two bits of *cosh* [wood]."

The younger man leant over and picked up two lumps of half-burnt wood. The old man threw the burning wood off the fire, scraped the red-hot ashes to one side, and then laid the two lumps of wood side by side in the bed of the fire.

" I canno' bide long in a tent or a waggon, young man, so I always looks after a bit o' fire," he said, as he carefully covered the two pieces of wood with the hot ashes. " When we gets back we'll want a warm."

The younger man went into the tent. After several minutes' angry shouting from within he reappeared, and the four of us set off along the lane. Presently we climbed through the hedge and made our way across the open fields. Before we reached the village, which we could see in the distance, the old man stopped and listened.

" I can hear some one running," he said at last.

" So can I," said the other gloomily. " It's those brazen children of mine."

The moon was coming up now and in a few minutes we saw a dark little boy and girl (the little violinist) tearing along after us. Their father spoke to them angrily, but it seemed to have little effect and when we reached the public-house they sat on the seat outside, looking very patient and virtuous. Before long, however, they crept into the bar and sat down by the door; the landlord did not notice them, and slowly they edged their way farther and farther into the bar, until finally they were both sitting over the fire roasting chestnuts on the hot coals.

"Have you travelled in Devonshire, young man?" said the old Gypsy, after his son had ordered and paid for four pints of beer.

"Yes, we were travelling with a little waggon in Devonshire last year," Christopher said.

"Did you ever come across my brother Adam Smith? He generally travels that country?"

"I seem to remember the name Adam Smith, but I can't recollect where I met him," I said. "In what part of Devon does he usually travel?"

"He's up near South Molton very often, my son."

"I remember him," said Christopher. "We met him on the road with his waggons. They were going to Honiton Fair."

I thought hard, but I could not recall the meeting.

"Don't you remember when we camped in that overgrown lane? When we had to cut the rose bushes and the nettles back, and——"

"Oh Lord, yes! When the *benglo dikkin mush* [devil-looking man] with the gun kept staring down the lane at us. We met him the same day we left that lane," I said, turning to old Mr Smith. "I remember he drove us up the road with a young chestnut horse; it had a long silvery mane. One of the traces broke and she very nearly put us all over the hedge. He breeds canaries in his waggons."

"That's right, young man, he breeds canaries in his waggons. If you go down to Devonshire this year I want you to tell him where I'm stopping. Can you read and write?"

"Yes."

" Then if you find my brother, you'll no doubt not mind writing a letter for him."

The man with the moustache put down his beer and rolled a cigarette.

" You spoke about an overgrown lane, brother, and a *benglo dikkin mush awvin* [devil-looking man coming] to you," he said. " Was that lane agen a little village called H——? "

" Yes, it was about two miles away."

" And how long did you bide in that lane? "

" Only one night."

" That man with the gun, brother, it's a wonder he didn't do you a mischief. He's like the devil himself. A very strange thing happened in that old lane."

" I know we didn't like the look of the *mush*," I said. " What happened? "

" You remember that the old lane crosses over the main road," continued Luke Smith, " and that there is a big new farm-house on the corner? "

" Yes."

" Well, that evil-looking man lives in that house. Six or seven years ago my cousin and his people were stopping in the old lane below the farm. His wife was going to have a *chavie* and if you can understand me, brother, she was lying in bed in the tent. They hadn't been there but two days when the farmer, who had been away, came back and made 'em put their horses in and shift. It was a pouring wet night, and, true as that fire would burn my hand, he made 'em take that poor unfortunate girl out on the roads. The next day she had her child and she died.

"My young cousin went nearly out of his mind, and that same night he and his brother went back to the lane and set the farmer's ricks and buildings alight. They didn't intend to fire the house, but the wind changed and the whole farm was burnt to the ground—house, barns, stables, and ricks. The farmer took the loss nearly as badly as my cousin did losing his little wife. He swore he'd murder a Romany for it. Except for strangers like yerselves, no travellers have stopped a night in that old lane for six years. The main of 'em thinks that man is the devil, brother."

When we returned to the Smiths' camp the fire looked completely dead, but when the old man kicked aside the ashes the wood buried in the hot embers lit up and in two or three minutes we were again sitting round a blazing fire.

"In the winter time when my children were small I always used to have a big tent with an open fire inside," the old man said, "and every night I used to back the fire in, the same as I did afore we went to the *livno-ker* [beerhouse]. If I stopped in one place a month, my son, the same fire would burn until we packed up and moved on."

We had not stayed long in the public-house, but it was getting late and we soon grew anxious to start on our return journey to Imber. The two men, however, insisted on our staying for supper, as they wanted us to write a couple of letters for them. We were persuaded to stay at last, and when the supper was ready we followed Luke Smith into the tent, where we found the family sitting round a big kitchen range. The old man's wife had gone to bed, but the young woman was busy preparing the *mass* and *moro* [meat and bread].

I am a vegetarian, and when I did not hungrily devour the fried meat and bread the woman seemed to demand an explanation. I told her that I did not believe in eating meat, but she was not at all satisfied until at last I gave her a reason for my aversion.

" When my mother married she was only a girl of about sixteen or seventeen," I said. " She was very fond of animals, and one day when, if you can understand me, I was made but not born——"

" Go on, young man, don't be afraid to speak your mind with us."

" She walked past a slaughter-house and saw a calf being killed. Afterwards she would never eat meat."

The woman and the rest of the family were deeply impressed with my explanation. I was allowed to give my meat to the dogs, and when I had been provided with a piece of cheese they told us several similar stories of children being influenced by incidents that at such a time had impressed their mothers.

" A woman in child has great powers," said Luke Smith thoughtfully. " For instance, you cannot lay an earth-bound spirit without an expectant mother."

I asked him what part an expectant mother played in the laying of an earth-bound spirit.

" She must be a young lawfully wedded woman bearing her first *chavie*," said Luke Smith. " She must go to the place that the spirit haunts with six clergymen, a spaded bitch, and a bantam cock. It may be out in a field. The six clergymen stand round the woman, who takes the ban-tam cock on her wrist and calls the spirit to her. When the spirit comes the cock begins to crow and the spaded bitch to wail. The woman asks the spirit what troubles its mind, and why it can neither rest nor leave the earth. It may be a very simple thing that troubles the spirit, or it may be something very deep that troubles the spirit—something so deep that neither the woman in child nor the six clergymen can understand. If they understand the spirit, they promise to put to right the matter that troubles it, they give the spirit their blessing and they sprinkle holy water on the grass. Then the six clergymen go back to their churches, the woman to her man, the cock to its hen, and the bitch to its kennel."

At this point in the conversation the kettle began boiling and the woman ' steeped ' the tea.

" The other day I was thinking what a simple little thing might worry a man after he is dead," continued Luke Smith. " I was out hawking with the pony and cart and I went into a public-house and ordered a pint of beer. Before I could get it down me an unlucky motor-car passed, it popped and banged all the way down the hill. The pony took fright and before I could catch up wi' her she tipped the cart over and broke one of the shafts. It was nearly an hour before I could get back to my beer, and when I was out in a copse cutting out a young ash-tree to make a new shaft I thought how unpeaceable it would have been if the pony had kicked my head off when I was getting her out of the upturned cart and I had died without drinking my beer."

When the food and the tea-things had been put away, the woman fetched a letter and, holding a candle by me, asked me to read it to them.

" MY DEAR SISTER AND BROTHER,

"We all hope that you and the children got back to your place safely after you left us. The frost was sharp and the roads was bad for the pony. I must tell you that Selina ran away with Algar Burton when we was all at the *kitchimir* [public-house] on Saturday night. They went down the country, they had a good pony and trap, but only a bit of a rod tent to lie in."

There were exclamations of " *Dick kie!* [Look there!] " and " *Dordi dordi!* "

"When I thinks it all over to myself, I believes we did wrong in keeping them apart. They've been after one another ever since the girl was fourteen. Dear brother and sister, you know as well as I do that when our young travelling girls does wrong it is because of her people keeping her from the man she wants. I knows that she is young to have a man, but I shan't go after them. They've gone and I trusts him to look after her well. I thinks I ought to tell you that she was *komm bori* [love big] before she left us, but, dear sister and brother, don't think that it was altogether her own fault, for he had a pretty little waggon and they wanted to get lawful married to each other months ago. If you see Selina and Algar, tell them what I've told you in this letter. Also tell little Isibel her bantams is doing well."

"My dear God!" said Luke's wife, as soon as I had finished the letter. "Now what do you think of that?"

"I thinks what I always thought," replied the man. "What did I tell Harriet? I told her that she was doing wrong in keeping that boy and girl apart. She tried to drive that poor young man away from the place. She tried to turn the girl against him. She ought to have known that she was doing the very thing that would draw 'em closer together. I knew what was wrong with the girl."

"So did I," said the dark little girl who had followed us to the village. "I knew that he'd broken her in."

"How did you know that, my child?" demanded the woman. "You seems to know a lot for a little one."

"You remembers that night when she come back to the fire, when she never said nothing, and never eat nothing, and just sat looking at the fire?"

"Yes, I remembers that, my dear."

"Well, little Olly and me was out a-wooding that afternoon," said the little girl. "She had gone for water, but we saw her go athawt the fields and meet him agen them willow-trees in the old green lane. That same night when she come up in the waggon wi' me, she bid and cried all night."

"That means nothing," said the man. "What makes you think he had her?"

The little girl grew impatient.

"Didn't I sleep wi' her, Dad?" she shouted. "Didn't I hear her crying to herself? Didn't I know she was bad afterwards?"

When the fate of the girl had been discussed for some time we wrote three letters, two for the old man and one for the woman, to the father of the runaway girl. After the letters had been addressed and sealed we prepared to leave, but before we fetched the pony and started on our journey Luke Smith offered to put us up for the night.

" There's no need to go back to your place if you don't want to," he said. " I've got a beautiful waggon and I can make you two beds fit for a king to lie on. Your dog shall be fed, and you shall have a good wash and a good breakfast in the morning."

✗ II ✗

When we left the gypsies' camp we had a walk of fifteen miles before us. We had already walked fourteen miles (not to speak of the distance we traipsed in Warminster). The moon came out and the pony clattered along the road and through the dimly lighted hamlets and villages; we took it in turns to ride and we reached Westbury at eight o'clock. Westbury, from what I have seen, seems a pleasant enough town, and although I question whether it has improved architecturally since Cobbett's days I imagine it has made great moral advances. He says·

> Westbury, a nasty odious rotten-borough, a really rotten place. It has cloth factories in it, and they seem ready to tumble down as well as many of the houses. God's curse seems to be upon most of these rotten-boroughs. After coming through this miserable hole, I came along, on the north side of the famous hill, called Bratton Castle, so renowned in the annals of the Romans and of Alfred the Great. Westbury is a place of great ancient grandeur; and, it is easy to perceive, that it was once ten or twenty times its present size.

We stopped at an inn in Westbury and drank two or three pints of beer before taking the road to Bratton, a distance of four miles. On the left, within a hundred yards of the road, the downs rise abruptly to a height of seven or eight hundred feet. Half-way between the town and Bratton the famous

Westbury White Horse is cut on the chalk hillside, marking the spot where Alfred the Great met and defeated the Danish host. In the eighteenth century the white horse was completely reshaped, and it seems that the renovator—disliking the shape of Saxon horses—chose his favourite hunter as the model. I feel, however, that we should not censure our grandfathers too severely, for recently the cutting has undergone a second ordeal, which, if not an attempt to give it the lines of a twentieth-century racehorse, has quite destroyed its appearance as an historical monument. It is strange how this misused horse has been subject to the national desire of keeping up to date. The edges have been cemented all the way round, and although it can be seen from a greater distance it looks very distorted from the road. But we must be thankful, I suppose, for what is still untouched, and remember that we may still walk upon the downs above, and listen to the wind hissing in the rough grass. In twenty years' time the White Horse will probably be illuminated by a hundred spot lamps.

We reached Bratton fifteen minutes before the inn closed. In view of the remaining seven and a half miles' walk over the bleak downs, we went inside and refreshed ourselves with another couple of pints of beer.

The clock struck ten, we untied the pony from the railings outside the inn, and inquired for the Imber road. It was little more than a lane and it wound its way at a steep angle on to the downs. We sat on the bank and rested several times, and when at last we reached the summit of the hill I began to give up hope of reaching the camp that night. Our feet were so tired we could scarcely stand, our legs

33   C

were aching and our eyelids were opening and closing like the eyes of drowsy goldfish. Standing on the extreme top of the hill we gazed helplessly across the downs.

Presently I noticed a cluster of straw ricks a couple of hundred yards away. I waved an arm vaguely and Christopher turned his heavy eyes and gazed vacantly in the direction to which I pointed. Without a word we left the road and stumbled across the hard frosty furrows of the intervening ploughland. There were two ricks built close together and we threw some loose straw in the gap which ran in between them. Christopher and the dog lay down, and I covered them up. I tied the pony to a post in reach of some barley straw and looked for a place to sleep myself. I found nothing comfortable on the ground, so I climbed to the top of a partly thatched rick, where I crawled into the straw and fell asleep.

When I awoke the moon had travelled a great distance across the sky. I was shivering with cold and, hoping that it was nearly morning, I listened for the crow of an early cock. Several minutes passed, but there was not a sound except the munching of the pony, the bleating of sheep, and the cries of peewits.

I lay still, wondering whether to call Christopher, then in the village below the downs I heard the church clock chime. It struck two, and again the downs were silent but for the animals and birds. When I called Christopher he did not answer, and, making up my mind to bear the cold for another hour, I lay back and looked up at the stars. I watched and thought about them for a while and, as I did so, my gaze seemed to penetrate farther and farther into the heavens. Each moment I discovered new and more distant stars and each moment the planets looked nearer, until I grew conscious of a strange upward motion. I felt as if I were being drawn from the earth. The great rick seemed to sway, and the harder I tried to throw off the weird sensation the more swiftly I seemed to rise. The air felt colder, and when I listened I could no longer hear the pony eating. I grew uneasy. Had I been struck by the moon? Were the stars drawing me from my body? Or had I died of cold?

Suddenly I heard a faint cry and I sat bolt upright in the straw. It was the voice of my brother. He was calling my name, and he sounded a thousand feet below me. I felt my foot. I felt the straw. It was all solid, but still the voice out of the awful distance kept calling. I crawled to the edge of the rick and peered cautiously down at the sleeping pony and the chalky downland soil only fifteen feet below.

" Hallo ! " I yelled.

" Hallo ! " echoed the distant voice. " I'm suffocated and frozen."

I was relieved to find that I was neither dead nor moonstruck and I crawled down from my resting-place. I wondered how Christopher could be both suffocated and frozen, but when I reached the gap between the ricks and found his legs protruding from a huge heap of straw I realized how easily the two things might happen at the same time. After uncovering him, I led the pony back to the road and we continued our journey to Imber. We passed a lonely farm-house where the dogs growled and the cows mooed, a pair of wild ducks got up from a dew-pond by the roadside, and as we walked along we could see the rabbits scurry away in the moonlight. When we reached the outskirts of the village a herd of heifers took fright as we approached the field in which they were grazing. They careered round and round, broke through the fence, and swarmed out into the road. We could do nothing to check the stampede. A whole line of posts supporting the fence collapsed simultaneously. If we succeeded in driving a few back into the field, they were out again before we had rounded up the rest.

Four or five heifers followed us into Imber, and before we had gone half-way through the village there was a hue and cry from all the animals in the fields, the farms, and the cottages. Our pony neighed—and every horse in the village neighed, galloped, and pranced. Our dog barked— and every dog in the neighbourhood barked. The heifers mooed—and every animal with two horns joined in a melancholy chorus. A billy-goat broke its chain and jumped into a paddock where three nanny-goats were quietly grazing. A cock crowed, and it was answered in the next garden, in the next paddock, in the next field, and the next farmyard. The din spread wider and wider until it could be heard far away on the downs.

We left the village and began to ascend to the downs below the camp. I had, of course, long given up riding the pony, but now I began to question whether I could walk on the ground any better than I could sit upon the pony. We paused to rest, and I sprawled on the bank so that my weight was distributed equally. I knew that if I sat I should be prejudiced against riding, and if I stood, prejudiced against walking. I finally decided to ride, and I asked Christopher to hold the pony while I mounted. I put my hands on her withers and as I sprang I cast my right leg over her back. (In the ordinary course of events I could sit on the pony and almost touch the ground with my feet.) I struggled desperately to reach my seat, my left foot hit my brother across the face, struck him again and again in the stomach and slipped to the ground, leaving my right leg poised across the pony's back. I sprang again, but I was too stiff to grip the pony with my knees; the momentum carried me over the other side, and I fell on my back in the road.

On reaching the camp we lit the fire and took the pony round to an old stable which we had already discovered among the ruins. It was an old loose-box, and when we were inside, unbridling and feeding the pony with a few crushed oats which we had bought in Warminster, I felt a sudden cold draught of air against my face. The stable door closed, plunging us into darkness, a white object glided in front of us, and I hunted my pockets for a box of matches while Christopher groped for the door-latch. If I had been able to find a match, or if Christopher had been able to open the door, we would have fled and spread a story which would have haunted the ruins for ever. In the pitch blackness, however, we fumbled and groped in vain. The white object glided in front of our eyes, and draughts of cold, clammy air fanned our faces. Christopher gave up looking for the door-latch and searched his pockets, one after the other, until he found three stray matches. He struck one on an empty box which I clutched in my hand, but it was immediately blown out. I shielded the second with my hands and we saw a barn owl circling round and round the stable. We opened the door and the great white bird glided silently out into the night.

The kettle was spluttering and hissing when we returned to the camp. We ate and drank and crawled into bed like tired dogs.

❧ III ❧

FEBRUARY IS, OF COURSE, THE GREAT LAMBING SEASON, and all over the downs the shepherds are kept busy night and day. Early in the morning I was awakened by the barking of sheep-dogs, the confused bleating of herded sheep, and the shouts and whistling of the shepherd.

A pleasant noise, I thought, as I lay back considering the look of the weather; a pleasant morning too, although a bit damp. A fine rain was blowing across the downs like a Scotch mist, making it a morning such as a mountain-dweller and a Wiltshire man loves, and yet curses.

Presently the shepherd whom we had met the previous morning came up to the door of the tent. " Hi ! " he called. " It's about time you young fellows was out of it."

" What's the time? " asked my brother, bobbing his head up.

" Five and thirty minutes past seven," answered the shepherd, examining a large Waterbury.

" Then we've only been in bed four and a quarter hours," grumbled Christopher.

" It was enough for Napoleon," I observed.

" It's not enough for me ! " he retorted, edging back into bed. " Napoleon could never have done a hard day's work. I've always suspected the man to be over-rated."

The shepherd caught sight of the bridle as Christopher spoke.

" I see you managed to get a pony yesterday? "

" Yes, it's tied up in an old stable round at the back," I said.

" I thought you'd get one in Warminster."

" Warminster! " I echoed bitterly. I gave him an account of our adventure and he promised to go round to the stable and feed and water the pony.

I did not go to sleep again and presently the temptation to examine the shaggy creature in daylight became too strong. I dressed and crept from the tent round to the stable. In the daylight the pony seemed even smaller than she had by night. She was a well-shaped little animal with a thick black coat and plenty of flesh on her back. A long sweeping tail gave her a certain elegance, but when I looked at her full, round body and at her attractive face I decided to name her Sally. I could not remember having seen a thin Sally. Sallys, like women in love, are always round and healthy.

I took her for a short run across the downs; then, collecting an armful of wood from the ruins of the farm-house, I returned to the camp, where I lit a fire and put the kettle on to boil. As soon as there was a cheerful blaze I called Christopher, who reluctantly crawled out of bed and dressed. The wind and the cold rain did not deter us from washing ourselves. The method we employed, however, was described by our grandmothers as " rinsing the bed off the face," which is to place your hands in any convenient receptacle containing water (in our case the cow trough), cupping them, drawing them rapidly up with as much water as they will carry, and swilling the water once and once only over your face, particularly your eyes.

I made a pot of tea, cooked the breakfast, and we sat down beside the fire. The shepherd presently returned to light his pipe. We understood that the farmer would soon be making his morning round, and we began to pack and make ready to depart so as to be gone when he arrived. But the shepherd assured us that so long as we did not pull up the fences or let our dog chase the heavy ewes, no one would mind how long we stayed. We offered him a seat, and after piling a heap of dry wood on the fire we fell into conversation.

" How long have you been on this farm? " I asked.

" I daresay since I was your age," answered the shepherd.

" You weren't born at Imber? "

" No, I was born in a village near Salisbury."

" We also are Wiltshire men."

" I should hardly have thought it."

I told him that we were born on the downs near Marlborough. " We are what are called ' dabchicks.' "

" Then you must come from Aldbourne? " exclaimed the shepherd.

" We were born," I said, " almost within a stone's throw of the pond near the green, which started the wars between Aldbourne and the neighbouring villages."

" I remember them," said the shepherd. " It was as dangerous to speak of ' dabchicks ' in a public-house near Aldbourne as to wave a red flag in front of a mad bull. I suppose you've never camped on these downs before? "

" No."

" I thought so, for most of the people with tents and vans stop in the track by those old stones. There are a lot of mushrooms about here in the autumn. I thought perhaps you'd got permission to collect the sheep wool off the bushes and fences."

He asked what we did for a living, and I told him that I wrote and my brother painted. I said, however, that I had made more money out of gathering wool and mushrooms than I ever had out of writing.

He was silent for a moment; then, taking his pipe out of his mouth, he said: " I would hardly expect you to believe that I wrote when I was a young man of about your age."

I could not help showing my surprise.

"Yes," he said, " it seems just as unlikely to me. I did, nevertheless, once call myself a writer."

I asked him countless questions about what he wrote, and presently he told us the following story. He spoke in a dialect which was only Wiltshire in accent:

" My father had a forty-acre small-holding on the plain near Salisbury. He was quite an ordinary small-holder, and except that I took more interest in schooling and in reading than my brothers I was an ordinary small-holder's son. If there had been room for me on the farm the idea of writing would never have entered my head; but as it was, soon after I left school, I started working in Sir Frederick R——'s kennels. I only went home three or four times a year, my wages were low, and I was very restless and discontented. I began to hate fox-hounds and everything that concerned hunting. I read in my spare time and spent most of my money on books. The more I read the more critical I became about the system under which I lived and worked, and the climax came when one day I quite accidentally bought a copy of Cobbett's *Rural Rides*. In the first twenty or thirty pages I found an almost perfect expression of my ideas. I had always wanted a farm of my own, but I had seen little possibility of ever getting one. Cobbett condemned the people who stood in my way, and who were responsible for the landowning system. I was determined to have my own farm. I saved up all my money and one day—forgetting in my world of reading my humble rank of kennel-boy—I went to my employer and asked him for fifty acres of barren land at the end of his estate. I told him that I would clear the land, cultivate it, build my own cottage, and pay him as soon as I began to turn over any money. He asked what the result would be if every young fellow discovered a whim for farming and wanted fifty acres of land given him. I said that I thought it would be a very good thing, and launched into a spirited argument on land distribution and the wrongs of estate ownership. He was surprised, I think, at my knowledge, but I was not very polite, and if he had not given me the sack I should have left of my own accord.

" I hunted for a suitable plot of land, and suddenly the idea of writing occurred to me. I would be a disciple of Cobbett. I was nineteen and I was confident that I would be able to make a living at writing. I found some cheap lodgings, bought all the books I could afford, and settled down to work. I studied for about three months, then I began writing for all I was worth. At the end of five months I began sending my articles and short stories up to various papers and magazines. They all came back. I knew that I was getting near the end of my savings, and I hurried over all the work that I turned out. Soon I only had three pounds in the world. I left my lodgings and set off on foot across Wiltshire. I began a novel as I wandered along, and I was just beginning to pick up a style of my own when I met a girl in a village about twelve miles from here. My writing took on a different importance. I only wanted to make money, and I went away promising I would return in six months.

" I wrote all day by the roadside and at night by candle-light in shilling lodging-houses. For months I nearly starved, but the hope of selling my work kept me going. Manuscript after manuscript came back, my novel was still a long way from being finished, and I began to get very depressed. I imagined the girl I had met surrounded by rivals who would go off with her while I was struggling at my hopeless writing. I could not concentrate on my work and I went back to her. It meant nothing to her whether I was a writer or a labourer. My last manuscript was returned, I was resolved not to lose her for the sake of a wild ambition, and I decided to give up writing.

" After a good deal of trouble I found a job on this farm. We got married. We had three children and—well, there was an end to my writing."

" It's certainly a peculiar story," said my brother when the shepherd had finished. " Did you ever think of writing again? "

" The War followed soon afterwards," he replied. " I

44

was away three years, and when I came back I was content with my life. When I got home at night I did not feel like locking myself away from my wife and children. My object in writing was to complain, and for that reason I doubt if I should ever have made any money out of writing."

The farmer appeared on his horse a few minutes later, and the shepherd got up and returned to his sheepfolds.

Mr —— raised no objection to our camping without his permission. We could no doubt have found an excellent place to settle on his land, but even if the War Office were prepared to allow us to flower (and perhaps go to seed) in the middle of a machine-gun range I doubt if we would have found the military environment altogether inspiring. The apprehension of impending death might, of course, have prompted us to stamp our names upon the earth while we had the chance. On the other hand, I fancy the continual coming and going, the popping and the banging and the clatter, would have been irksome and even distracting when the ditties of the larks and peewits were drowned by the mighty voice of a passing mechanized unit or a pessimistic sergeant-major.

I learnt that the farmer bore the same name as a man mentioned in the inscription on a stone which was erected just under a hundred years ago on the road from Tilshead to West Lavington.

At this spot Mr —— of Imber was attacked and robbed by Four Highwaymen in the evening of October 21, 1839. After a spirited pursuit of three hours, one of the Felons, Benjamin Colclough, fell dead on Chilterne Down. Thos. Saunders, George Waters, and Richard Harris were eventually captured and were convicted at the ensuing Quarter Sessions at Devizes, and transported for a term of fifteen years. This monument was erected by public subscription as a warning to those who presumptuously think to escape the punishment God has threatened against Thieves and Robbers.

I did not ask Mr —— if the victim of the robbery was his grandfather, but as the name is not common I suspected that he was a relative.

When the farmer left us we took down the tent and began packing. We had, of course, no pack-saddle (not even an old harness pad) for securing our baggage on the pony's back. We fetched her from the stable and looked despairingly at her, the countless bundles of bedding, canvas clothes and heaps of pots and pans. The tent and the blankets were packed, and when they had been roped down securely we hung the milk-can, the frying-pan, the axe, the kettle, and the saucepans on either side. Beneath the great load the pony looked extremely small; she swayed from side to side as she breathed, and when she moved forward the utensils rang a peal as if to hail the start of our journey. Our first aim was to get off the War Office territory, and having been told about a Roman road running from Imber across the downs to Heytesbury, we decided to make for there and then across the Wylye Valley up on to the southernmost end of the Plain, which, we were told, was a wild and deserted country.

As we approached Imber, the bus, which runs to Imber only once a week, rounded the corner out of the village and drove headlong into a group of chickens crossing the road. There was a fluttering, a cackling, and a screech of brakes;

46

the bus sped on up the hill, and when the dust settled a dead cockerel lay in the middle of the road.

We left Sally to eat the grass on the roadside and went to examine the bird.

" If we leave it here," said Christopher, picking it up, " it'll be run over by a lorry or eaten by a rat. If we put it in the hedge the rightful owner will probably never see it."

" You're quite right," I said.

" Is there anyone looking ? " Christopher asked, putting the bird under his coat.

In the village we stopped at the old public-house and tied Sally to a ring on the wall. The landlord greeted us sullenly.

" Not much of a day," I said cheerfully.

" I'm thinking it wasn't much of a night either," said the landlord.

I asked him what was wrong with the night.

" Well, there were two Gypsies with a pony and dog who came through the village about half-past one this morning. I don't know exactly *who* they were, but they frightened Farmer B——'s heifers so that they broke down fifty yards of fencing and got out on the road, my billy-goat broke loose and got on every mongrel nanny-goat in the village, all the dogs started barking, and nobody in the bloody village got a wink of sleep. Now, what can I do for you? "

I ordered two pints of beer, and asked the landlord if he would have one himself as a slight compensation for the escape of his pedigree billy-goat.

Having emptied our mugs and left the landlord in a better temper we made our way up a lane leading through the back of the village, past the church and out on to a narrow rough track. It was a steep climb, and before we had gone far we were alarmed to find the load gradually slipping down the pony's back.

"Hold on to it," cried Christopher, who was leading Sally. "We'll get round this corner so that we can repack out of sight of the village."

With a great deal of shouting and shoving we managed to get round the corner, but instead of finding ourselves alone we were face to face with a hedgecutter, who was sitting on the bank eating his dinner with his wife and children. The whole family stared at us in surprise, and when we drew level with them and the load slipped off the pony's back on to the ground, their expressions changed to sheer astonishment. Before we could disentangle the ropes Sally began kicking in a frantic effort to free herself. This brought the man out of his apparent trance, and jumping up he helped us clear the maze of ropes and blankets and pots which were wrapped round the pony's back legs. When we had dragged everything away there was a strained silence, broken at last by a repressed giggle from the children. The woman looked at them and exploded in almost hysterical laughter.

"It's a pity you haven't an old saddle or pad," said the hedgecutter when the woman's laughter subsided.

"Yes, but since we haven't," said I, "what do you think we'd better do?"

"Well, if you tied something tight round the pony's belly there'd be less danger of yer stuff slipping."

"What would you suggest?"

" I should put a sack over the pony's back and then lace it tight with cords."

I told him that I did not understand.

" Well, have you never seen a pair of corsets on a woman? "

" No," I said.

The hedgecutter carefully explained. His description, however, gave me a stronger impression of what a woman looked like in corsets than what corsets looked like on a woman. He helped us lace the sack on the pony and repack our belongings.

After steadily ascending for nearly two miles we came out on to a fine open stretch of down. Here and there were hazel copses and occasionally a great clump of beech-trees The downs were rather more rugged than most parts of the Plain, the grass was long and looked as if it had been unkept and uncut by sheep or man for many years. Scores of rabbits scurried away at our approach, and overhead the peewits, having already split up into pairs, twisted, turned, and uttered their strange, wistful spring cry.

Before long we came to a notice-board on which was written :

DANGER, LIVE SHELLS

DO NOT TRESPASS ON THESE DOWNS

Christopher halted and gazed curiously at the notice. He said that he would not have expected people to be so casual about high explosives.

" It's probably the War Office way of stopping trespassing," I said. " A farmer writes ' MAD BULL ' on his notice-boards, the War Office write ' LIVE SHELLS.' It's reasonable. They couldn't say ' SAVAGE GUN,' ' MAD TANK,' or ' BEWARE OF THE COLONEL.' "

A couple of hundred yards from the notice-board, however, I saw a pointed object protruding from the ground. We went up to it cautiously and found that it was in reality a live thirty-six-pound shell. Not far away was a second and in the neighbouring copse a third. The place was strewn with them and had they not been rusty and half covered with earth, I should have ventured to compare the War Office with the reptiles who used to set man-traps and spring-guns in their woods and their pheasant preserves. But soon an explanation dawned on us. They were relics of the War, experimental shells which, having failed to explode when they had crashed into the earth, were now considered proof against a meddling rabbit or a wandering schoolboy.

After a mile or so, the downs began to drop again, the track became less rugged, and on the left were great ploughed cornfields. The rain started again. We began to feel hungry and cold and we decided to stop for dinner. There were no copses or sheltered places now, but presently we came to a straw rick where we tied up the pony and lit a fire with old rick spars. I filled the kettle from a trough near by, and Christopher threw a bundle of straw on the ground against the rick.

" I only hope a spark doesn't set the rick on fire," I said, watching the wind blowing the white-hot ashes in all directions.

" It's all pretty wet," said Christopher, lying back in the

straw. "I don't suppose anyone will come up here this afternoon."

He had scarcely finished speaking when I heard a noise in the lane. I peered round the corner of the rick and saw a big saloon car approaching. It was too late to put out the fire, and as we were sitting with our back to the approaching car we stayed still and hoped that we would not be seen. A few minutes elapsed, then I heard the ticking of an engine behind the rick and saw the radiator and bonnet of the car slowly appear. With a feeling of sickening guilt we watched two men get out and walk round to the place where we were sitting. I was about to get up and offer an apology when suddenly they pointed to a sheepfold across the road and, tucking up their coat collars, walked rapidly away. When they returned carrying a sick ewe they climbed into their car and drove away.

As soon as the fire was out we packed away the dinner things and led Sally back on to the road. We walked steadily along until it began to get dark and we reached an old chalk quarry beside the road. There was plenty of grass for the pony, and in the farthest corner, sheltered from the wind and rain, was a little alcove cut deep into the chalk bank. The entrance was about twelve feet across, and inside there was sufficient room to pitch a small tent and light a fire. There were four great straw ricks in the middle of the quarry; against one of these stood a milk churn (evidently ready to be taken up to the sheep) containing ten or more gallons of clear water, and at the farthest end of the quarry was a pile of rotten pine poles. Sally was unpacked and tethered on a long rope. The hard chalk stone made it difficult to pitch the tent, but with the help of the *cavie saster* [kettle iron] we managed to get the rods firmly in the ground, the bottom of the tent filled with clean dry straw, and the beds made ready for the night.

When darkness descended over the downs we were sitting at the foot of the tent waiting for the kettle to boil. The rain and wind hissed through the grass above the quarry, but where we sat not a drop fell, nor a breath of wind stirred. The red flames of the pine wood reflected on the chalk so that the whole of the alcove was lit up with a warm red glow. When the fire blazed the wall around us shone with the same bright hue; when the fire sank to a red glow the whole atmosphere changed to the same deep tone. It shone on our faces, on the tent, and gradually disappeared into the sullen blackness overhead.

As the evening progressed the wind dropped, the rain cleared off, and the stars came out. It was still little after eight o'clock and, finding that we had no milk left for our breakfast, I decided to walk to the nearest farm.

A mile below the quarry I saw several farm buildings, partly hidden from the road by a wood. I followed a narrow track until I came to three lofty thatched barns and a farmhouse, and was about to cross the yard when I heard a ferocious growl and the rattle of a chain. In the darkness I could just distinguish a huge Airedale preparing to spring, and instinctively I began running. The chain evidently was very long, for after several yards I felt the dog still close behind me, and, to make it worse, in a final effort to get away I slipped and fell headlong on the stones. Expecting the dog to spring on top of me I covered up my face and lay still, and then to my great relief I found that the dog had reached the end of its tether. When I rolled away and stood up the dog raved and gnashed its teeth until, afraid that it would break loose, I hurried across the yard to a passage, where I was met by a man and woman evidently disturbed by the commotion. The man held a hurricane lamp up to my face.

"What is it you want?" he asked, looking suspiciously at me.

"A pint of milk," I said.

"Is it you camping up in the old quarry?"

"Yes," I said, a little surprised that he had seen us.

"My son saw the fire, and told me that some Gypsies were there. You'll have to be careful not to set those ricks alight."

I assured him that we would do no damage. The woman took the can, and when she had gone into the house I asked the farmer why he kept such a savage dog.

"It's an out-of-the-way place, young fellow," he answered. "Some years ago we had a hundred chicken stolen. I said from now on I'd keep a dog that would frighten every one off."

I assured him that it certainly succeeded in frightening me. "Did you ever find the people who stole your chicken?"

"To tell the truth, young fellow, for a long time we thought it was some of your kind. A big gang was camping that very night in a lane about a mile from here. The police got hold of the right men, and of course we found that they'd waited for some of your people to stop agen us."

"I'm very glad they were caught," I said, "for a lot of our kind of people get blamed for things which they know nothing about."

"I know that," he said. "How many horses have you got up there?"

"Only one pony."

"How would you like a bag of hay for it?"

I thanked the farmer and he led me up to a barn, where he filled a sack with sweet clover hay. Then groping about under a reaping machine he produced four eggs, which he told me to put in my pocket.

"How much do I owe you?" I asked when we returned to the farm-house.

"Twopence," said the farmer.

I thanked him again, and asked if we were safely off War Office property.

"Yes, the boundary-line is at the far end of the quarry. Good night, young fellow. I'll hold the dog while you go by."

Throwing the bag of hay over my shoulder, I stumbled along the track and out into the lane where the moon helped me to see my way back to the camp. When I reached the quarry I was greeted by a neighing and a snorting, which rang out on the chalk walls and echoed away over the downs. I put out a feed of hay for Sally and was about to pick up the sack again when I was startled by a sudden commotion which broke out in the camp. I left the pony and hurrying forward was alarmed to hear a succession of loud reports, like the cracking of rifles. A piece of fire shot up into the air and soared above the quarry, something whistled past my face, and in the camp I found Christopher doing a sort of war dance round a tremendous fire, which every few seconds sent out a shower of sparks and flames.

" What is it? " I cried, shielding my face from the missiles which were flying in every direction. I was thinking of the unexploded shells.

" It's the fire bursting the chalk stones."

A moment later a pot began to boil and splutter its contents over the fire. As the flames and the heat subsided the explosions died down, and all was quiet again.

I examined the fragments of chalk stone which lay strewn about the camp. " If we made a big enough fire," I said, " the whole quarry would go up."

Christopher swung the pot off the fire and took out the bird which the bus had killed. " I put in a few potatoes and carrots to give it a taste," he said.

We ate in silence, and when we had finished my brother said lazily: " You are a vegetarian usually. How is it you eat chicken to-night? "

" Chickens," I said, " aren't usually killed by buses. My objection is to eating animals systematically bred for food; to eating an animal that has been begotten, carried, born, suckled, and cared for until it has grown large enough to be slaughtered. The existence of a slaughter-house is significant. It waits for the bull and the cow, the ewe and the ram, not to produce life but carcases. A short time ago I was talking to a young gypsy who had taken a temporary job in a slaughter-house. His wife was going to have a *chavie* and he wanted some money. He told me that after sticking the job a fortnight he was so disgusted one night that he threw it up and found work on a farm. One night the slaughterer brought back a cow that was dying in calf; the cow was killed, cut open, and the calf removed, a few minutes later to be stuck for veal. That emphasizes the whole point of my opinion."

" I agree with you there," said Christopher, " but you haven't explained why you won't kill a rabbit."

" I won't kill a rabbit or a bird because I am a sentimentalist. It is my personal feeling. I don't attempt to say that wild animals should not be hunted for food."

Christopher gazed into the fire and smoked, and presently he asked if the farmer had objected to our camping in the quarry.

" No," I said, " I think we could leave the tent here to-morrow and walk on to the downs on the other side of Heytesbury. The War Office property ends here."

" And where shall we leave the pony? "

" We'll take her with us. I believe we'll find a good place on those downs."

" The greatest difficulty," Christopher said, " will be to persuade some one to sell us a piece of ground, rather than to find a suitable place. We shall want an extra couple of acres so that we can keep the pony and perhaps a cow."

" I don't see any reason why we shouldn't make ourselves entirely self-supporting."

" We could at any rate make our own butter, bake our bread, brew our beer, and grow our own vegetables."

" If I had, like thousands of men, no ambition beyond making a livelihood, I would beg or steal a piece of land and make myself entirely independent by growing

56

my own food, tobacco, brewing my beer and building my house."

" Most people thirst after respectability too much to enjoy a life like that," replied Christopher. " They inherit the urge, and it carries them through the dullest work with the zeal of a young poet. They'll sweat all day in a stuffy office so that at night they can return to a house in a respectable street and a not less respectable wife. They don't enjoy their houses any more than they would cottages, and they don't enjoy their refined wives any more than they would ordinary country girls. I——"

" Stop a minute! I hear a clock striking," I interrupted. " Ten o'clock."

" That must be Heytesbury Church," said Christopher, yawning. " We'll go to bed early to-night."

I changed the pony to a fresh piece of grass and climbed up to the top of the quarry. The moon was shining with the intensity that only comes in the winter, and on the slopes lying below me I could distinguish the smallest objects, even the flash of the peewits' wings. About a mile ahead the downs sloped up again, forming a sharp ridge, on the extreme top of which a line of tall beech-trees gave to the surrounding country a solemn grandeur, unique in the non-mountainous parts of England.

I looked down at the camp fifteen feet below. The fire was still burning, and the pony, having eaten her fill, came up to the tent and lay down. I took a last look across the downs, then I threw away my cigarette and went to bed.

❧ IV ❧

THE MOMENT I AWOKE IN THE MORNING AND HEARD A skylark singing above the quarry, I did not have to open my eyes to know that the sun was shining. It seemed, indeed, that so long as the bird kept singing the sun would remain out.

I like the skylark more than any other bird in this island, and next—without any regard to music—the curlew and the plover. Most people like particular birds because of their associations, not because of their song, their shape, their colour, their flight. The woman who raves about the song of the nightingale invariably has a deeper-rooted affection for the twitter of a sparrow or the cawing of a rook. The curlew, the peewit, and the skylark belong to the open type of country—the country where I was born, and which draws me from the softest valleys to the bleak downs and moors.

> The trees are few, but they are always bent by the wind.
> The flowers are scarce, but always sway in a gentle breeze.
> The cries of the birds are wild and almost melancholy.

The quarry was flooded with sunlight, and from the opposite hill, where the rooks had started repairing their nests in the beech-trees, there came the usual excited cawing and fluttering. One or two flies, misled by the warm sun, buzzed about; a butterfly, suffering under the same illusion as the flies, flew overhead and alighted on the chalk stone. Even I found it difficult to believe that two months, probably of frost, snow, rain, and wind, would elapse before the trees would be in leaf and the grass long.

I gave the pony a drink of water, and when we had breakfasted we made ready for our walk on to the downs across the valley. I collected a bundle of wood for the evening fire and filled the kettle. Then a quarter of an hour, according to our calculations, before opening-time Christopher fetched the bridle and mounted the pony.

A mile down the lane we passed the hospitable farm with the savage dog, and then as we descended into the valley we were surprised to hear the church bells ringing.

" Why are the bells ringing? " said Christopher with concern.

" Because it's Sunday," I answered.

Christopher stopped the pony.

" If it's Sunday," he said, " we'll not be able to get a drink until twelve o'clock."

I pointed out that we had not long to wait.

" We'll sit on the bank," said Christopher, jumping off the pony. " There's plenty of grass for Sally to eat."

I lay down in the grass and lit a cigarette. " I think one can contemplate God," I said, looking at the church, " almost as well up here as down there. The bells sound pleasant from here. A bird must see our church in a very favourable light. They look down on it, like us, on a Sunday morning when the sun is shining, and they hear the bells ringing and they see people walking all in one direction. They have never been inside and they know nothing of ecclesiastics and politics."

The chewing of the pony against my left ear became almost deafening and I sat up. Grass grew in abundance on the bank, but Sally was bent on eating the grass under my head.

"I wonder who occupies the front seats in the church this morning," I went on.

"The owner of the estate here," replied Christopher drowsily.

"Yes, unless he has his own chapel." I thoughtfully plucked a blade of grass. "It's astonishing," I said, "with what dignity it is possible to worship."

Christopher went to sleep and when he awoke he looked about him and suddenly said that the country was beautiful.

I pointed to the estate which spoilt what otherwise would have been a very beautiful piece of country.

"Why, in the Devil's name, is park country so peculiarly unpleasant?" he exclaimed.

"There is," I said, "such an atmosphere of reverence."

"That is exactly what it is intended to inspire," replied Christopher. "Did I ever tell you about the Rumanian Gypsies who camped in Lord C——'s main drive?"

"No. Who told you about them?"

"The landlady of the Greyhound at Plough. The Rumanians—I believe it was the same lot that we met in Cornwall—were travelling on the road near Plough late at night. The horses and the women were dead-beat, and they decided to camp on the first promising piece of green. On their left ran a wide grass verge and a high wall. None of them could read the notice-boards which forbade camping, and, but for a ditch dividing this verge from the highway, they would have pulled off the road straight away. Presently they reached a flat piece of closely cropped sward with no ditches, no notice-boards, only two immense wrought-iron gates. They drew their waggons and traps off the road, tethered their horses, pitched their tents, and made themselves comfortable for the night. When they awoke in the morning they felt that something was wrong and hastily lit their fire in order to get their breakfast over before a hue and cry was raised. It was still early, but when the women and children got up and the commotion of breakfast began in a camp of thirty Gypsies, the alarm was given and the news ran like wildfire throughout the startled and indignant household. The footman saw lines of blue smoke drifting away from the partly hidden entrance of the main drive; he opened the window and, instead of hearing the peaceful cawing from his lordship's rookery, caught the distant shouting and laughter of women, the yelling and screaming of children, the barking of dogs, the neighing of horses, and above the din the occasional voices of men. If he had immediately reported this to the butler —I was told—the matter might have been kept from his lordship's ears. He closed the window and hurried through the great house, passing the news to every one.

" His lordship dressed and went downstairs. He was irritated to find all his young guests up, discussing the whole affair and clamouring to put the Gypsies to flight. The nobleman refused to encourage their bravado and sent for his gamekeepers, while the butler telephoned the police-station. When the *veshengroes* [gamekeepers], carrying twelve-bore guns and leading three mastiffs, arrived in the camp, the

Gypsies invited them to sit down by the fire and eat and drink. The keepers, at last, impressed the intruders with the magnitude of their offence and told them that they would be arrested at any moment. The spokesman of the Gypsies became very apologetic and asked the head-keeper to explain to his lordship that it was past midnight when they had made their camp, and that in Rumania wrought-iron gates were but a monument to a vanished aristocracy. They harnessed their horses and moved off, and the great man allowed the matter to drop."

Christopher closed his eyes and yawned. " The landlady of the Greyhound explained that the offence would not have been quite so grave if his lordship had not at that moment been entertaining a house-party."

It was on the stroke of twelve when we reached the village and tied the pony outside the inn. We waited until the clock had finished striking, and when no one unfastened the bolts we rapped upon the door.

" I'll be annoyed," said Christopher, looking up at the windows, " if there is no Sunday licence in the village."

At this moment, however, we heard some one approaching, and when the bolts had been pulled back the door was opened and we were led into the bar. I ordered two pints of bitter and the landlord was about to draw them from a beer engine when Christopher interrupted and changed the order to two bottles of India Pale Ale.

" Why," inquired the landlord after we had paid him, " did you change your mind about the beer? "

" I never like to drink beer from an engine when I'm the first customer in the morning," Christopher replied.

" You're no doubt thinking of lead poisoning? "

" Yes," Christopher admitted. " I believe there are very few publicans who throw away the first pint which they draw in the mornings."

" I don't blame you for being careful," the landlord said. " I always throw away the beer which stands in the pipes. I don't, however, see how a man could get lead poisoning from one pint."

" I don't suppose he would," said Christopher, " but it may make him ill for a day or two. I heard of a nasty case in Bath."

The landlord wiped the counter and put away the empty bottles.

" A man was ill for months—I believe years—and when he was finally taken to a hospital the doctors said that he had been suffering from lead poisoning. They asked him, at last, if he was in the habit of going to the public-houses when they opened in the morning. He admitted that he was not only the first customer in a public-house every morning, but every evening. He was asked if there was a beer engine in the public-house which he frequented. There was, and it was found that the beer in the pipes had never been drawn off after standing at night."

" It's a wonder it didn't kill him," exclaimed the landlord. ' I shall be glad when the brewery takes out these engines and gives me a place for the barrels behind the bar. Ah, good morning, Robert! What is it, a Guinness? You'll need summat sustaining, won't you? "

A young man of about twenty-five sat down beside us. " No, George, a pint of beer will do for me."

"I should have a drop of stout," said the landlord. "I tell you, my boy, you'll need it. I went on Guinness for a fortnight before I was married. Doctor's orders!"

"Very well," said the young man, throwing a sixpenny piece on the table, "give me what you like for that. I don't care what it is, so long as it's a pint."

"Then, Robert, I'll treat you myself. It's most important to keep up your strength, my boy, most important." He poured two bottles of Guinness into a pint mug and handed it to the young man. "Now mark my words," he continued, "if you have ten or twelve of them to-day, you'll be very glad of it, very glad indeed you will. On my honeymoon——"

The young man grinned at us. "If you don't shut up, George, it'll be you who'll be wanting the Guinness. Good luck!"

"May you pull through, Robert!" the landlord said, opening a bottle for himself.

The young man drank a long draught of his Guinness and, turning to us, asked if it was our pony outside the inn.

"Yes," I said.

"Have you come far this morning?"

"No, we're camping in the quarry on the Imber lane," I answered. "Can you tell me how far it is to the downs on the other side of Sutton Veny?"

He said that it was between four and five miles, and when he understood that we were walking he offered to lend us a trap and a set of harness for the day.

"It belongs to the last tenant of my cottage. He won't mind so long as you bring it back to-night."

NELL

I thanked him and asked how far away his place was.

"About five minutes' walk. When we've had a drink or two we'll take the pony there."

Christopher took a pinch of snuff from the ounce tobacco tin on the table. "When are you getting married?" he said, softening the note of curiosity in his voice.

"To-morrow morning."

The landlord, who was standing by the window, suddenly called our attention. "If you look across the road, you'll see his bride," he said. "I tell you what, she's the prettiest wench in these parts."

We went to the window. The landlord was certainly not far wrong, for along the opposite side of the road walked a beautiful, black-haired, rosy-cheeked country girl, leading a small greyhound puppy on a string. She did not appear to be more than fifteen or sixteen, but she looked as strong as a lioness.

I never think it requires a fortune-teller to predict that a girl fully developed at fifteen or sixteen will be a mother before she is twenty.

When she was out of sight I congratulated the young man, who we found to be a waggoner, and called for some more beer to toast his beautiful bride. He said that he believed he would like the travelling life and that he intended one day to buy a horse and caravan and take to the roads indefinitely; his Violet (whose grandfather was reputed to be of Gypsy descent) was not indifferent to the attraction of the Romany *jivimus* [life]. The only drawback was the difficulty of making a livelihood on the roads.

"If you wish to lead more than a hand-to-mouth existence," I said, " I advise you to save up your money before you go travelling. Without a little capital you cannot buy a cheap horse and turn over a couple of quid. To-day it's difficult to make a living on the roads. A man, however, who understands farm work can always get jobs as he goes along—hoeing, dung-spreading, haymaking, hopping, strawberry and pea-picking, sheening [threshing], and harvesting. The old Romany trades such as basket-making, broom-making, and tinkering have been killed by the cheap bazaar."

The waggoner looked ready to ask a question, but after I had taken a draught of my beer I went on again.

" A woman can generally sell wild flowers in the towns " —I was thinking that Violet would look beautiful selling wild flowers. " In the late summer there are mushrooms to gather. On every rubbish heap there are shillings' worth of bottles, jars, rags, iron and brass. A tent and a wood fire will become a home, but peace and security—as the Englishman knows them—will not go with the life. As soon as you have a horse-waggon and a silk handkerchief round your neck, you'll find that two-thirds of the people in the world are against you. At nearly every lane end you'll find a gamekeeper, a landowner, a farmer, or a policeman."

We finished our beer and accompanied the young waggoner to his cottage. It was an old four-roomed, thatched, and stone-built cottage, beside a stream in a low meadow outside the village.

" I don't think I should want to leave a house like that," I said as we made our way along a footpath across the fields.

" I thatched the roof," said the waggoner with evident pride. " I bought the cottage dirt cheap and did it up myself. Violet did the papering and painting."

When we reached the cottage we were shown the kitchen and the parlour. In the kitchen there was a big, old-fashioned open range, a plain deal table, wooden chairs, white cotton curtains with pink roses, and a large, solid-looking dresser. A plain, clean, cosy kitchen in which to eat and smoke. In the parlour I was glad to find none of the usual semi-Victorian trappings; there were no leather-covered sofas or chairs, no aspidistras, no fire-screens, and none of the abominable cheap modern furniture which nowadays seems to leak into nearly every young couple's household. The young waggoner and his Violet had furnished their parlour to be lived in, not to be looked at; a parlour where in time their children could play before the fire without being told not to mark the brass fender with their hands, nor the linoleum with their feet.

We went upstairs to the bedrooms. One was empty, the other had a rug, a pair of pretty curtains, a bowl of wild flowers (which the waggoner said his Violet had picked that morning), and last but not least a double bed, pulled up near the window so that it commanded a view of the surrounding fields.

When we returned to the kitchen Violet had arrived and was unpacking some china and arranging it on the dresser. She was a little shy when we were introduced, but very soon she was showing us the greyhound puppy that her younger brother had given her for a wedding present, and feeding the pony with apples and bread and lumps of sugar.

She raced up and down the garden with the pup, displaying that curious mixture of childishness and womanliness peculiar to girls of her age. In some ways her maturity and sense of responsibility were far greater than her lover's, but with little prompting she would have made running jumps at him and climbed all the apple-trees in the garden. He was obviously in love with her, and Violet—in common with all women—had not been long in discovering his surrender to her : she was aware of the advantage this gave her, and it was fascinating to watch her practise it.

It was twenty minutes to two when the waggoner led us to the shed at the back of the cottage and showed us the trap and the harness. The trap was of the open type, and, after deciding that it was not too heavy for the pony, we harnessed her and backed her into the shafts. Whether Sally had been broken in for harness we were then unable to say, but the moment Christopher climbed into the trap, the moment she felt a pair of wheels moving behind, she pricked up her ears, reared, and in a fraction of a second changed from the lazy, easy-going pony to the ensnared animal. Before either the waggoner or I could grab the bridle, the trap, the harness, Sally, Christopher, and everything but his hat disappeared through the garden hedge. When we reached the gap and clambered into the field we saw the whole turnout making off in the direction of the village brook.. It happened so quickly, so alarmingly quickly! One moment Christopher was commenting vaguely upon the quality of the reins, the next he was gone. A flash, a yell, a hat falling gracefully to earth, a gap in the hedge !

Violet left her puppy and followed us through the gap
in the hedge. I looked at her when she joined us ; was she
going to laugh? Yes—no! Her eyes shone, they blazed,
her lips parted, she put her hands on her stomach ready to
protect herself against the overwhelming laughter which
threatened to overcome her. Then suddenly her expression
changed, a tiny cry escaped from her lips, and I looked
across the field. While feasting my eyes upon Violet I had
almost forgotten my brother's danger.

" The reins have broken ! " cried the waggoner. " He's
bound to go in the brook now ! "

I started running, so did Violet, the waggoner, and the
puppy. In the nick of time the pony turned, but disaster
still seemed inevitable. The right wheel of the trap lifted
higher, higher. Christopher flung himself half over the side
like the side-car passenger in a T.T. race. The wheel
lowered, and they were off again.

" Keep over this way," the waggoner yelled to me,
" we'll try and head 'em off ! "

Bearing slightly to the right the pony rounded the field
and in a few moments was galloping straight at us, the trap
swaying from side to side and occasionally lifting bodily
off the ground. The three of us spread out and waved our
arms furiously. Would she stop, or would she career
madly over us? Judging by the thunder of her hoofs, the
snorting from her nostrils, and the determined gleam in
her eyes, the latter seemed the most probable. But no, she
was going to try and avoid us ! I was on the outside and
she was attempting to go wide of me. The more I ran, the
more treacherously she bore to the right. I saw the nettled

look in her eyes as she glanced from side to side, then I realized the fatal decision she had taken. She was going to pass me on the inside. The weight swung from the right wheel to the left and the trap turned over. The pony's legs kicked in the air, and everything converged into a mass of kicking legs, wheels, and reins.

I flung myself upon the pony's head. The kicking subsided, the upturned wheel spun round despondently, but where was Christopher? I looked round and saw that Violet and the waggoner were picking him up. He could walk, and together the three of them came hurrying to help me with the pony.

" Keep behind her," Robert was saying, " or she'll kick yer head off ! "

With a great deal of tugging and pulling, the traces were unhitched. Then the breeching straps and the belly-band. The trap was dragged away, and the pony, trembling and shaking, sprang to her feet. The splashboard, the seat, and the door of the trap were smashed, Christopher (walking round in brief circles) groaned and rubbed his shin-bones, but before long we were all making our way back to the cottage. I was pulling the trap, Violet leading the pony, and Christopher and Robert the waggoner walking behind discussing whether the pony had ever been broken in.

When we left the cottage we passed through some pleasant marshy country, low and divided by rivers and brooks. It is only a narrow stretch of country, perhaps not a mile in width, but pleasing in its direct contrast of meadow-land and dry chalk downs.

Except for the scenery we passed nothing of note on the road to Sutton Veny. Of course there was Tytherington, the headquarters and kennels of the Wylye Valley Hunt. It is a typical hunting village. Everybody looks like either a foxhound or a horse, everybody is either dressed in riding breeches and polo shirts or white smocks. Everybody carries a crop in some shape or form, and everybody's voice is either clearly Cockney or clearly county. It is a pretty village.

As we had stayed a long time with the waggoner and Violet, we hurried on to the next village, where, we had been told, the public-house closed at two o'clock. We were both famished when we arrived, and on entering the inn we were disappointed to find that it was seven minutes past closing time. After a short discussion with the land-lady, however, she agreed to serve us with bread and cheese and two cups of tea. Would that do? Yes. Then would we please take the pony off the pavement and go round to the back? After tying Sally up in the yard we went into the kitchen, where we sat down beside the fire and were presently served with two generous plates of bread and cheese. The cheese, of local make, was strong and tasteful but not rank ; the bread was home-made, and the shallots home-grown. It would have been an enjoyable meal if we had been able to keep our eyes off the row of pint tankards hanging on the kitchen dresser and the barrel of beer which was just visible in the passage. Discreetly we hinted at our dissatisfaction, but before a tankard could be taken down or the barrel tapped there was a resounding crash in the yard. We hurried out and were alarmed to find Sally wrestling with a length of drain-pipe which she had dragged from the wall of a shed. There had been no railing or post or ring in the yard, and foolishly we had tied the pony to the rainwater pipe of the coal-house.

" What a damned trouble you people are ! " said the landlady, coming to the back door and looking at us with disgust.

She swore as well as any woman I have met, but after we had propped up the drain-pipe and finished our meal she cut us some sandwiches and let us have a bottle of beer to take away. Christopher, who was still stiff from the excursion of Friday, fell off the pony when he was attempting to mount outside the inn. Fortunately he was seen only by an old woman and a small girl, and when he had remounted we made our way through the village until we reached a white chalk road leading on to the downs.

A couple of hundred yards below the top of the hill we reached a square enclosure, packed tight with lambing pens. The coops ran right up the road and inside sported the newly born lambs. Their movements were so absurdly funny that Christopher got off the pony and we sat on the grass bank and watched them. There was one lamb with a jet black face and black legs, and every few seconds— without the slightest provocation—he would abruptly catapult himself into the air and then gaze at us with profound solemnity. His object in life, it seemed, was to test the force of gravity. His twin brother was a frivolous lamb who spent his time in climbing the hurdles, pretending to butt his mother accidentally, and making ridiculous sallies at everybody and everything. In the next pen there was an inquisitive lamb who pushed her nose through the hurdles and sniffed and stared at us with a look of earnest inquiry. The floors of the coops were filled with dry straw and the tops covered with a crude but effective thatch. Out of twenty or thirty lambs there were not two of the same temperament, but in contrast to these intensely lively little creatures was a sick lamb sitting in a corner of the pen by itself.

A mile beyond the summit of the hill we came to a gate. The hard road ended there, and we struck off across the downs on a rough grass track. The country now was really open and wild, there was not a house in view, the downs (a mixture of the Salisbury Plain country and the more rugged Marlborough Downs) rolled away on either side, and the only habitation in sight was an old shepherd's van. There were clumps of gorse bushes, some brilliant in yellow flower, and the trees—which were mostly hawthorn—were bent by the prevailing south-west wind.

On the summit of a hillock, in the midst of this great loneliness, we found a clump of thick and particularly fine gorse bushes. They grew in a circle about two hundred feet in diameter, in the middle of which was a round patch of smooth grass, like a circus ring. We had entered through a gap in the bushes, and inside the rabbits had trimmed the grass so short that it looked like a soft green carpet. We calculated that it was close on tea-time, tied the pony to a bush, sat down on the grass, and opened the sandwiches and the bottle of beer. Had we not found the perfect spot? A thatched wooden cottage in the middle of this ring of gorse bushes, on the top of this hillock, a house hidden yet commanding a view of the downs on one side and the valley widening out into the lowlands of Wiltshire on the other.

Standing on the top of an ant-hill I could see Warminster in the extreme north, and as I stood there the faint sound of the church bells reached my ears. I listened. The wind was coming from that quarter, in gusts, one moment blowing fresh and warm against my face, the next quite still. With the wind came the sound of the bells; as it freshened the sound became just audible, then as the final gust swept by the bells were loud and distinct as if the church was at the foot of the downs. While I listened a skylark sang overhead, and as if in sympathy with the bells it varied the length of its song as often as the wind rose and fell.

When I stepped off the ant-hill there was but one thought in my mind; it was the importance of living on top of that hillock, in the middle of that ring of gorse bushes. It was the one place on the earth where I wished to live. Enthusiastically we paced up and down the grass. We mapped out the foundations of our home, marked the position of the windows, the fireplace, the stables, the garden, and a little way down the hillside we found a clear dew-pond. There was everything we wanted. And with a horse and trap we would be able to shop in Warminster every Saturday.

We lay on the grass and allowed our imaginations to run wild and to build up their exquisite castles in the air. Vision upon vision floated up in my mind, faster, stronger, wilder. At last we had found the perfect place in which to live.

It was almost dark when I mounted the pony and we set off down the hillside from the ring of gorse bushes. We took a different route back, and after cutting across the open downs for about a mile we came out on an old Roman road. For five or six hundred yards the lane ran through a narrow copse of ash-, pine-, and oak-trees. The pines and the oaks, thickly covered with ivy, still afforded a great deal of shelter, and as I was thinking what a fine place it was for 'travellers' (Gypsies) I looked down and saw a white patch of ashes and the usual signs of a recent encampment. Straw lay scattered about where the tents had been, fragments of coloured rag fluttered from the hedge, and shavings and half-burnt sticks were strewn around the fireplace.

Instinctively I leant down and held my hand over the ashes. I felt no heat, and less cautiously I pressed my hand into the bed of the fire ; there was just a faint warmth ; the travellers had gone in the morning.

" Not many horses," said Christopher, glancing up and down the lane. " It looks as if they only spent the one night here."

Farther along we passed several more fireplaces, then the lane narrowed, and we began to descend into the valley. On the right was a high chalk bank covered with dry uncropped grass, and on the left—upon the slope of an almost sheer hundred-foot drop—a copse of leaning and twisted pine- and ash-trees. " It will be pleasant here when the blackthorn and the dog-roses are out," I thought to myself as we stumbled down the rough track.

Under the slopes of the downs the fields were ploughed and harrowed, waiting for the oats and barley sowing. " What will happen to the nests," I said, looking up at the peewits, " when that field is rolled ? "

Christopher glanced in the direction to which I pointed. " The farmers and waggoners often take a lot of trouble over the peewits' nests," he said. " I remember seeing a nest moved to the edge of a field, and after ten minutes the bird went to the eggs and continued sitting. On two occasions I've seen a horse suddenly stop and refuse to go over a nest."

As we walked along, Christopher resting his hand on the pony's back (there was no stirrup leather), I began to think of the white ashes and a story my father told me when I was a child. " It's fortunate he did tell me," I said to myself, " for sooner or later I would have learnt a painful lesson ! "

One peaceful afternoon in the summer my father was riding along a country lane looking for some Romany friends who were travelling in the district. He came to a large green verge, where he saw a white patch of ashes in the grass. " I wonder how long they've been gone," he said to himself as he reined his horse. He dismounted and led his animal to the spot, where he bent down and plunged his left hand into the ashes. For a second he held it there, then with a shout he sprang to his feet. The ashes were white-hot. He caught up with the travellers round the next corner, but his hand was in bandages for a fortnight.

He was always doing things of that nature, and when I am told that I greatly resemble him I always hope that I shall continue to benefit from his experiences. Had he ever closed a cupboard door without something falling directly upon his head? Certainly he never shut a door without banging it, and was often himself responsible for the carelessly placed book, typewriter, or melodeon which fell on his head, but nevertheless he did seem to get more than his share of ill luck. Whenever a small boy threw a banana peel on the pavement, my father was sure to be walking boisterously up the same street. When a coalman left a grating open, he was sure to be at hand. But again I make an admission. He always walked along with his head in the air, either thinking how to begin the next act of his new play, or how interesting or stupid was the face of the man or woman across the road. I could spend hours relating his strange misfortunes, from the occasion when his trap hit a boulder and upset Mr George Bernard Shaw in the roadway to the dreadful stir when he blew up the bathroom geyser.

It was pleasant walking and reflecting in the moonlight, and after resting for an hour in the public-house at Heytesbury we made our way back to the camp. We cooked a good supper and sat beside the fire until nine o'clock, when we undressed and went to bed. I lit a candle and stuck it on the bottom of a saucepan, then I took a small copy of Marlowe's *Dr Faustus* and read the last act before going to sleep.

V

WE WERE UP JUST IN TIME TO SEE THE SUN DISAPPEAR behind a ridge of heavy storm clouds. There was a strong north-west wind blowing, and altogether it was a very different day from Sunday.

"Anyhow," said Christopher, crawling out of the tent and sleepily fumbling for some straw to light the fire, "I don't care what happens so long as the rain holds off."

"Nor I. We'll have a little breakfast and then pack up," I said. "It'll be sheltered in the gorse bushes whatever the weather is like."

By the time we were packed and ready to start it was gone ten o'clock. The wind was still strong, but the clouds had lifted and there seemed little prospect of rain. We made our way out of the quarry by a path which we had not used before, and we were surprised to see an enormous shell lying by the roadside. It was thrown up on the bank just as an awkward stone might be cast aside by a road-man, and as I looked at it I could not help thinking what a novel form of suicide it would provide. A man would only require a sledge-hammer and a smattering of golf.

The landlord of the public-house in the village was amused at our method of transport, and after talking with him for an hour we went on to a shop a little way up the road and purchased our requirements for the next three or four days. Before we had left the village far behind we heard the church bells begin ringing. They were ringing, we gathered, for the marriage of the young waggoner and Violet.

We had considerable difficulty in ascending the steep track on to the downs, and when at last we reached the copse where we had found the old fireplaces we were hungry, the wind was perishing, and we decided to stop for dinner. We coaxed the pony into a clearing sheltered by bushes and thick undergrowth and made up a good fire. There was a rick of hay in the adjoining field and after Sally had been provided with a good feed we sat down and waited for the kettle to boil.

The north wind shrieked through the trees above us and we made no attempt to move during the afternoon. We smoked and read and talked, and it was not until it began to get dark that we stirred ourselves.

Once more we were packed up and on the move. We kept along the Roman road for a mile, then struck off across the downs in the direction of the hill where the ring of gorse bushes grew. In the open, the wind was freezing and so strong that it was difficult to walk against it, but at last our destination was in sight. I have seldom been more thankful for shelter. We hurried in through the little gap like Arabs before a sandstorm. Christopher had brought a sack of hay from the place where we had stopped for dinner; there was water for the pony in the dew-pond, we had filled the kettle and two bottles from a trough, and now the storm could rage to its heart's content. When we had unpacked we tethered the pony and hurriedly collected a heap of dead gorse wood. There was no moon, but by a great effort we managed to get the tent up, the lamp lit, and the fire burning before it was pitch dark. All the evening we sat over a blazing fire listening to the awful shrieking of the wind. The pony fed almost in the camp, and Nell, half frightened by the noise, sat between us staring nervously into the black void beyond the firelight.

During the night the storm abated, and in the morning when we awoke the sun was shining and the birds singing, as if with redoubled energy.

As soon as we were dressed Christopher took the kettle and set off to the field where yesterday we had found the water trough. I busied myself with the fire and the breakfast, and I had hardly been alone ten minutes when I was startled by the furious bellowing of a bull. I left the fire and went out into the open, but the field from which I heard the noise was hidden by a row of trees. The bellowing grew louder and presently I sent Nell back to the camp and hurried down the hillside. When I was clear of the trees I saw the bull, its head down, charging madly across the field and my brother running towards the water trough for all he was worth. "Maniac!" I cried to myself when he reached the trough and calmly proceeded to fill the kettle.

He started back for the gate, but now the bull was heading him off.

I ran towards the field. The trough was in the corner, and my aim was to get over the fence and attract the attention of the bull while Christopher made a bolt for the gate. I pulled the red silk handkerchief from my neck when I was inside the field and waved it frantically at the bull. The demonstra

ROMANY ENCAMPMENT

tion succeeded in annoying it, but instead of coming at me as I intended, it renewed its attack upon my brother. I moved gradually nearer to the trough, and at last the bull gave me his attention. He put his head down, and the moment he began to charge Christopher bolted for the gate. I had not far to run, but nevertheless I lost no time reaching the fence and leaping back into the lane.

As Christopher climbed over the gate and disappeared behind a clump of bushes the bull smashed its way through the fence and careered down the lane towards him. Between the trees I caught a glimpse of Christopher walking unsuspectingly along the lane, but a moment later he was making a hurried retreat to the gate. He jumped back into the field and while the bull bellowed and pranced against the gate I waved my hand and he (still carrying the kettle) ran past the trough and joined me in the lane. We hurried, needless to say, over the second fence, and went back to the camp, mingling relief with a fear that Nell might have stolen our breakfast which I had left uncovered in the frying-pan.

Later in the morning we walked across the downs to some sheep pens, where we found a shepherd who told us that the bull had been caught in the village an hour after our adventure, and that the land was owned by a gentleman farmer whom we would see the next morning in a green car. His name was Crane and we gathered that he had taken up farming not because he liked it, but because he thought farming a respectable means of subsistence. We understood that he came from a good family and that he was educated at a university; but it was his cleverness in discovering the respectability of farming that aroused my admiration. Is there one other profession in which one may openly claim to be a gentleman? I've never heard of a gentleman timber-merchant, a gentleman painter and decorator, a gentleman grocer, or a gentleman haulage contractor.

VI

THE DAY WENT ON PEACEFULLY. NO MR CRANE, NO PRY-
ing gamekeeper, no policeman showed himself on the
downs, and at five o'clock when we put the kettle on for
tea everything pointed to the day ending in the intense
peace and calm with which it began. We sat over the fire
smoking and talking and would have gone on doing so all
the evening, had we not been disturbed by an odd clattering
which at intervals we heard in the distance.

The noise seemed to proceed from the distant downs
where, as far as we knew, there was no habitation of any
kind. We left the fire and walked through the gap in the
gorse bushes, where from the hillside we could survey the
surrounding country. It was almost dark now, but although
the noise came more clearly we could see nothing save the
outline of the hills.

As we stood watching and listening, above the clatter
and the jingle we began to distinguish the shouting of
men and children. Then from behind a hillock, evidently
upon the track of the old Roman road, appeared a dim
moving light. In time this was followed by a second,
a third, and at last a fourth. The men's and children's
voices were joined by the yelping and barking of dogs,
then the striking of horses' shoes upon the rough stones
became distinct; and soon the little string of lights was

winding its way along the old Roman road directly beneath us.

In the twilight we could just distinguish the shape of two large living-waggons, two traps, and six or seven horses. They passed on down the lane and presently disappeared behind the pine- and ash-trees which sheltered the spot where, two days before, we had found the fireplaces.

" I wonder who that is? " said Christopher gazing at the last light as it disappeared behind the trees.

" When they've had time to put up their tents and have their tea, we'll walk down and find out," said I.

At half-past seven we shut up the tent and walked down the hillside to the lane, where we stumbled along in the direction of the camping-place. When we reached the trees and had turned the sharp bend to the right we found the camp only a few yards ahead. Two fires were burning, one on either side of the lane, and in the flickering light I could see the waggons pulled in and the tents pitched against the hedges. The forms of men and women and children crouching over the fires were just visible, but before they saw us approaching a greyhound slunk out from underneath a trap and growling viciously stood in our path; a colt tethered to the hedge took fright and after breaking loose careered into the camp, dragging the chain behind.

In a moment the occupants of the camp sprang up from the fire; a boy caught hold of the dog and a man the colt.

The man came forward. " I didn't think to see anyone up here to-night," he said suspiciously.

" We're stopping just across the downs," Christopher

replied. " We saw you pass, and we thought we'd come down for a bit of company."

" You've got tents up there? "

" Yes."

" Then I am sure you are welcome, my brothers," said the Gypsy. He released the dog and looked at us more closely. " You isn't on your own? "

" Yes, only the two of us."

" No women, nor wives nor nothing? "

" No, God help me," I said smiling.

By this time the family from the waggon on the other side of the lane had gathered round and were looking at us with intense interest. A dark girl, struggling to keep a hold on the colt with a rope which she had slung round its neck in place of the chain, came forward and two immense dark eyes gazed at us. A fairer girl, holding the hands of two small children, also joined the circle and surveyed us critically.

" Was you here yesterday? " inquired the man who had first spoken.

" Yes, it was about midday when we got here."

" Did you come this way? "

" Yes, we ate our dinner in those bushes over there."

" And there was no other traveller in this old lane? " said a youngish woman who, holding a baby to her bare breast, appeared at the front of a low rod tent.

" No," replied Christopher. " There was no other traveller when we were here."

" He's *lelled* [caught]," exclaimed the woman with the baby. " The *muskeros lelled lesti* [police caught him]."

"Don't worry yourself, my sister," said the man. "I'll drop down dead afore I don't find him."

"Didn't you notice that fireplace?" asked the dark girl timidly.

"I noticed it the day before when we were walking this way," I said, mystified by the travellers' behaviour.

"You did?" demanded the girl, her eyes suddenly blazing.

"Yes," I answered. "I put my hand in the ashes to see how long it had been left."

"And how long had it?"

"It was just warm. I should think it had been left early in the morning."

The girl's eyes suddenly filled with tears, and she pushed the colt back and disappeared out of the firelight, dragging the animal behind her.

"Who is it you are looking for?" I inquired, without showing half of the curiosity that I felt.

The man hesitated. "*Awve adray* the *yog dudee* [come into the firelight]."

We did as he directed and for several seconds he looked seriously into our faces.

"I knows you can *jin* the *pukka* [understand Romany]," he continued at last. "I thinks you is travellers, but if you won't be offended wi' me, I thinks you is strange travellers."

We smiled. "There are several reasons why we might seem strange to you," I said. "For one thing we read and write and for another our parents died some years ago, and for several years we lived in a house."

" You mean to say you've no father or mother? "

" No."

" I am sorry," said the man. " It's bad to be like that when you are young. But it is because you are scholars that you are different. I can see the blood's there; and now I wish you'd both make yourself at home. Sit down by the fire and my woman shall make you some tea."

A fine red-haired woman who hitherto had not spoken picked up the kettle and hung it on the iron over the fire.

" Caroline ! " called the woman. " Break up some sticks and put them on the fire ! "

The dark girl appeared again and knelt down on the grass. Her long black hair hung in front of her shoulders, and as she broke up the sticks she bent her head low so that her face was almost hidden. Presently she put her head to the ground and blew the red embers of the fire until the sticks caught, and then I saw that she was still crying.

The man who had now sat down beside us was also watching the girl sombrely.

" You see that girl," said he. " That's my brother's child. That woman with the baby over there is my brother's wife."

The girl bent her head lower and pushed her hair forward.

" What are you crying for, Caroline? " continued the man. She did not speak and then he turned to us. " She is crying because she thinks she has lost her father."

" What's happened to him? " said Christopher.

" Well, now that I've spoken a few words with you, I'll tell you; but, excusing me for my ignorance, I couldn't be sure who you was at first. The police are looking for

my poor brother, and if they catch him they'll be bound
to hang him."

"Why?"

"Well, if you can understand me, brother, he committed
a very serious crime without meaning to do no wrong,"
replied the man, beginning to roll a cigarette. "If you
listen to me, I'll tell you exactly what happened.

"Last Wednesday, that's five days ago, we was on the
roads all day from seven o'clock in the morning until six
at night. We went from A—— all the ways to H—— in
the Forest. When it began to get dark we tried to stop
in three different green lanes and each time was turned
away before we could take the horses out of the waggons
or make a drop of *peeameskie* [tea]. Well, it rains and it gets
quite dark, but at last we comes to a wide green lane wi'
plenty of grass for the horses and a nice sheltered place to
pitch the tents.

"Natural enough, we is all perished and famished
and greatly in need of a cup of tea—particularly me
brother's wife, 'cos she'd the baby sucking from her
all day.

"We pulls the waggons off of the road, plugs the horses
out, puts up the tents and lights the fire. Then we all sits
round waiting for the kettle to boil.

"My brother's tent was pitched close to the fire and
Freedom, his wife, was sitting at the front, with the baby
on her knee and the food basket open before her. We was
all so hungry that we didn't know how to wait for our
vittles; and then suddenly, as I goes to take the kettle off
and make the tea, the *veshengro* [gamekeeper] blustered up

like a great bull and said, ' Who the bloody hell gave *you* permission to camp here? '

" Before we had time to answer he began a-hollowing again. ' Put that bleeding fire out,' he shouts, ' and clear off, before I call my men and throw the lot of you out! ' "

The man leant forward and savagely threw his half-smoked cigarette away.

" I up and told him straight that we wouldn't move, and he lifts up his boot and he kicks and scatters the fire all over Freedom, the poor little baby, and the tea-things. The straw bedding in the tent catches alight, and my brother, stamping it out, cried, ' If you put your ugly foot in that fire again, blood-eyes, God blind me, I'll kill you! '

" The gamekeeper takes not a bit of notice. He lifts up his boot, lets fly, but instead of kicking the fire misses and hits the kettle. The boiling water splashes over Freedom and the baby. My brother's blood runs to his head. He goes like a madman, same as you would if you saw your woman or child treated the same. He picks up the kettle and smacks it across the gamekeeper's head, and the boiling water spills down his neck and all over his clothes. Down the keeper drops like a block of wood and for a minute we all thinks he is *mullo* [dead].

" Well, after a bit we pulls the *mush* round, but soon as he comes to and finds how he is scalded and where he is, he begins a-hollowing and shouting and jumping up, runs away down the lane as if the Devil were after him.

" My sister-in-law cut off some bread and meat, gave my brother all the money she had, and he ran off into the woods to hide. Not ten minutes after he'd gone a car with twelve *gavmushes* [policemen] inside came a-tearing up the lane. I told Freedom to slip out of the way so that I could say as they'd both gone. But before I could open me mouth they collars me and takes me off to the police-station. Then after they'd questioned me and found that I was the wrong man, they let me go and started looking for me brother.

" Since the next morning we've been on the move. The police have surrounded us twice in the middle of the night. They are thinking that he will come back, or that he is sleeping wi' us at night and hiding during the day. Yesterday I met my cousin's boy who said that my brother was wi' his father, and that they had stopped down in this old lane."

The woman with the baby spoke as soon as the man had finished.

" He ought to have stayed by himself, he's bound to be *lelled* [caught]. They'll hang him or transport him for sure. Oh, *dordi dordi*, what shall I do? "

" There is," I said, " one thing you need not worry about. They can't hang him, nor can they transport him."

" Excuse me, young man," said the Gypsy, whose name we now discovered to be Ira Lovell, " they can hang him. My great-grandfather was hung for less than that, and if they don't hang him they'll be bound to transport him."

" You can stake your life on it, they can't," I said. " I don't know much about the law, but I know enough to assure you that they can neither hang nor transport him."

The red-haired woman came forward. " The young man

is quite right, Ira. Things are different to what they was when your great-grandfather was hung."

"The most they can do is to put him in prison for a while," Christopher said. "In the circumstances I doubt if they would even do that. The great difficulty is that you have no outside witness."

"Was the baby badly scalded?" I asked.

"Her dear little feet was blistered wickedly," said the woman.

"Did you show them to the police?"

"Yes," answered Ira, "they wrote that down."

By this time the kettle was boiling, and the red-haired woman, having made the tea, handed us two mugs and two hunks of bread and meat.

"And how many horses have you?" asked Ira, thrusting aside with an effort the subject of his brother's misfortunes.

"Only one pony," I answered.

"Have you no waggon, then?"

"No, only a little rod tent just big enough to lie in at night."

"And how long are you going to bide here?"

"Well, we thought of getting a piece of ground here, so that we would have a comfortable place to *hatch* [stop] during the winter," replied my brother.

"You don't intend to move very far yet a bit?"

"No, not until the summer."

"I was only going to say," said Ira, "seeing as you are on your own, you would be welcome to come along with us. From what I know of you, I likes your company;

and I make no doubts I could put things in your way. You could come strawberry-picking with us. Two young fellows like yourselves could earn good money."

I was just about to answer when through the trees I saw a light moving quickly in our direction. Before I had time to point it out to Ira, the dark girl, who had been gazing across the downs, stood up and called her mother. We all left the fire and followed the girl into the middle of the lane, where we stood watching the approaching light.

"Listen!" whispered the girl. "I think I can hear a pony galloping."

A few moments elapsed and then the beating of horses' hoofs became audible, the light disappeared behind the trees and then suddenly came into view again on the bend of the lane, only a few yards ahead. A thick bay pony, covered in white sweat, drew up almost upon its haunches.

"It's my cousins!" cried Ira as the firelight shone upon the two men who were seated in the trap.

The black-haired girl took the pony by the bridle, the men slung the reins across the animal's back and sprang out of the trap.

"Who is this?" said the elder, pointing to us.

"Two young travelling fellows. They are camping a little ways from here. Where's Namaya?"

"That's what we come about."

"Is he all right?" asked the dark girl almost in a whisper.

"Yes," answered the man. "He's along wi' Father. He come to us in the middle of the night and asked me to look for yer mother. We've come over sixty miles to-day."

" Not with that pony? " exclaimed Ira.

" No, we chopped wi' Leonard Buckland on the way."
The man turned to the woman with the baby. " Namaya
says he wants you to stop along wi' Noah until the spring
comes; then you've got to sell me the waggon and the big
mare and go on down to Cornwall with the children. He
is going to find Richard Cooper. Come a bit he'll get
Richard to write to Father and I'll let you know where
to meet him."

The woman listened in silence and then returned to the
tent.

" Have you had anything to eat? " said Ira's wife,
tapping one of the men on the shoulder.

" Not since we was at Leonard's place."

" Well, sit down, my cousins, and I'll find you some
vittles. Caroline! Unharness the little pony and put him
on that spare plug chain in my trap."

I helped the girl with the pony, which was rather a
lively little animal, and Christopher having mentioned
the hayrick escorted Ira there with two sacks. When
the pony was dried down, rugged, and watered, we
returned to the fire, where the cousins were eating their
supper.

" You are in no hurry to get back to-morrow? " said
Ira to the elder of the two men, when he and my brother
returned with the hay.

" We are," answered the cousin. " I've got to let
Namaya know Freedom and the children are all right
afore he goes on down to Cornwall. We ought to start
away as soon as it is light in the morning."

" You'll have your own pony back when you gets to Leonard's place? "

" Yes, he said he'd feed her up and have her ready in case we came back."

" Well, if that's the case," said Ira, " I'll put up a tent and make a bed ready, or you'll not get a bit of sleep afore it's time to start off again."

Ira took the kettle iron, and I helped him set the rods and lay the sheet over the framework. Then we filled the bottom of the tent with dry straw, and the red-haired woman, bringing blankets from her waggon, made the bed.

It was now past eleven o'clock, and, seeing that the new-comers were ready for bed, we said good night and prepared to leave. Before, however, we could depart from the encampment we had to shake hands with Ira, his wife, the cousins, each of the children, and faithfully promise to visit them again in the morning.

Ira accompanied us past the horses and repeated his wish that we should in future travel with him; we returned to the camp, where we found that the pony had devoured most of the hay from beneath our bed.

❧ VII ❧

At nine o'clock in the morning, having shaved and eaten a hurried breakfast, we walked out on the hillside and watched for the arrival of Mr Crane. An hour passed, then in the distance there appeared a dark speck which soon we were able to distinguish as a car, its colour privet green.

On the old Roman road about a third of a mile from our camp the car stopped, and out stepped Mr Crane. We saw the shepherd walking to meet him, but Mr Crane, instead of making his way to the sheep-pens, opened the back door of his car and took out what appeared to be a pair of field-glasses.

" He's seen Ira's waggons," remarked Christopher.

Evidently he had, for after standing with the glasses focused in that direction he returned to the car and drove towards the encampment.

A quarter of an hour must have elapsed before the green car reappeared. The shepherd was standing at the gate, and, after a short conference during which he and Mr Crane pointed in our direction several times, the car swung round and bore down on us.

" I expect he's told Ira to clear out," said Christopher.

" Yes," I answered drily, " I expect he's going to make a job of it by telling us to do the same."

The car pulled up at last, and Mr Crane lowered the window.

" Good morning," we said politely. " You are Mr Crane? "

" Yaas. What did you want to see me about? "

" I should like to explain why we are here," said Christopher, putting one foot on the running-board and one hand on the door-handle, as if to prevent Mr Crane from getting away. " I am a painter——"

" Artist," I murmured, vaguely thinking that Mr Crane might conclude that I was the decorator.

" And my brother is a writer," continued Christopher, disregarding the interruption. " We are both fond of solitude and this type of country, and we would like to buy a piece of land and live here for the next three or four years. The spot where we are camping is almost perfect, and we hoped that you would be able to rent us a few acres on which to build a wooden shack."

Mr Crane's expression foreshadowed his answer.

" I'm sorry," he said, " but I'm afraid that would be out of the question. What chiefly concerns me at the moment is that you are camping in these gorse bushes when they are required for sheltering my ewes."

I felt an impulse to point out that if every ewe chose a separate growth of bushes there would still be enough shelter for them all, but before I could speak Mr Crane opened the door of his car and stepped out. He was a youngish man of perhaps thirty, loose-limbed and of medium height. His face was of the open type and his features as evenly proportioned as the colours in a school tie. He was dressed in riding-breeches, leather gaiters, and a greenish Scotch tweed coat, but it was his headgear that attracted most of my attention. It was a hat known as a 'pork pie,' and although I knew them to be worn by County people I had never (this was a year before they became popularized) seen one on the head of a farmer. The colour of the hat, oddly enough, was bright green. Whether Mr Crane intended the similarity I do not know, but it matched the car so perfectly that I was inclined to think that he either bought the hat to go with the car or the car to go with the hat.

"You don't seem to understand," he said, walking to the gap and surveying our camp, "that I have to work for my livelihood. This is lambing time. You're keeping the sheep away from this shelter and I cannot afford to lose livestock. These gorse bushes don't grow here by accident, they are cultivated for a purpose."

"I suppose you have no objection to us remaining here to-day?" I said, speaking with more politeness than I felt.

"I'm afraid I have," replied Mr Crane. "I've given you my reasons; but I'll give you permission to camp for two nights elsewhere. Come over here and I'll show you."

He led us round the gorse bushes and pointed to a spot two or three miles across the downs. "If you stay there you must keep your dog under careful control, and remember I've only given you permission to camp for two nights."

The spot did not look very inviting, but we thanked Mr Crane, who without further comment returned to his car and drove away. His refusal to let us build had made us depressed, his refusal to let us camp had made us angry, and we both grew very irritable until at last I pointed out that he, as a landlord, would have made the place not worth having at a gift. If Mr Crane objected to Ira camping in the Roman road, he would surely object to Ira and his relations visiting us. "We would have to live and choose our friends according to his conventions," I said. "We would have to consult Mr Crane before we made a single alteration to our place. We would have to consult him before we brought home an extra horse, or cow, or dog. We would live in continual fear of incurring his disfavour. It would be Mr Crane this, Mr Crane that——"

"Mr Crane can go to the Devil for all I care!" said Christopher as he ripped off the tent sheet.

The pony was caught and stood solemnly eating the grass while she was loaded. The ropes were secured about her belly and the pots and pans hung on either side. We glanced wistfully round the strange ring of gorse bushes and led the pony through the gap.

In the lane we found Ira and the rest of the two families sitting round a fire making clothes pegs. The work was done to a strict routine, and the speed with which the pegs were fashioned, strung together, and piled in the hawking baskets was astonishing and a contrast to our own efforts at that fascinating art. Ira, seated upon the ground, the back of his 'peg knife' held against his raised knee, began by shaving the lengths of newly cut hazel-wood, which lay in a bundle beside him. Instead of running the knife down the stick in the fashion of the ordinary whittler, he held the back of the blade against his left knee, and, taking the stick in his left hand, drew it up and down the sharp edge of the knife until one half of the length was skinned. The stick was then tossed in the air, the finished end caught, and the remaining half of the stick shaved.

As he worked he sang the very old stanzas which, according to George Borrow, the Gypsies of Wandsworth sang (with varying words) as they sat before their tents making skewers.

> Can you *rokra* Romany?
> Can you *fake* the *bosh*?
> Can you *del* the *vesher*
> While *mandi chores* the *cosh*?
>
> Can you *rokra* Romany?
> Can you *fake* the *bosh*?
> Can you *dick* the *gavmush*
> While *mandi chins* the *cosh*? [1]

---

[1] Can you speak the Gypsy tongue?
Can you play the fiddle?
Can you fight the keeper
While I steal the stick?

Can you speak the Gypsy tongue?
Can you play the fiddle?
Can you spot the policeman
While I cut the stick?

George Borrow's version of this song is as follows:

> Can you *rokra* Romany?
> Can you play the *bosh*?
> Can you *jal adray* the *staripen*?
> Can you *chin* the *cosh*?

This, translated literally, means:

> Can you speak Romany?
> Can you play the fiddle?
> Can you go inside the prison?
> Can you shave the stick?

I think the change from the prison to the more rural 'keeper' is in-

Next to Ira sat his small son, a boy of about eight years. He held in his hand a chopper, and directly his father had finished shaving a stick he took it, laid it upon a block (which was also a jig), and cut it into three lengths, each of which was calculated to make two pegs. These shaved and divided lengths were then handed on to the beautiful dark girl who sat with her legs crossed, her black hair falling loosely over her shoulders and her black eyes fixed solemnly on the sticks which she was binding with strips of tin. This tin was secured with small nails, and the bindings were fixed one on either side of the middle of the length, so that when it was passed on to the red-haired woman she was able to split the two pegs before they were divided.

The process of splitting or opening the peg is rather intricate; the knife has to be forced into the centre of the grain and twisted until the split almost reaches the tin binding. The blade is then turned in the split, the back of the knife placed against the knees, and the inside of the peg shampered. Two quick strokes finished each peg, and the length was passed on to the younger and fairer girl (the

teresting. Ira Lovell's version has a distinct flavour of the country, whereas the version of the Wandsworth Gypsies is influenced by the town.

> Can you *del* the *vesher*
> While *mandi chores* the *cosh*?

These lines mention the fight with the keeper while the wood is being cut, then, later in the second verse,

> Can you *dick* the *gavmush*
> While *mandi chins* the *cosh*?

the look-out for the constable—or sometimes the *bori rye* (the landowner) —while the newly cut wood is being shaved and the green bark hidden.

daughter of Ira) who divided them with a small hook
chopper before passing them on to her little sister, who
strung them on a strip of willow and laid them, gross upon
gross, in the hawking baskets of her mother and her aunt.

Ira—indeed, the whole encampment—was nothing
short of astounded at the way in which we travelled. The
youngest children, with no shoes and practically no clothes,
were playing in the lane. They stood still and gazed at us
open-mouthed; even the black-haired girl raised her eyes
for a moment and smiled, first at us, then at her mother;
but Ira himself looked deeply concerned.

"My dear brothers," said he, looking gravely at the
bundle underneath which the pony was barely visible,
"have you no trap?"

"No," I said smiling. "A week ago we thought it an
advantage to be without a trap, but the day before yesterday we found that we had no choice."

"I don't quite follow you," replied Ira.

"The young man," said the red-haired woman, "means
that there is a reason why they are without one."

I explained the affair with Robert and Violet and our
pony.

"It was lucky you wasn't killed," said Ira, examining
the pony's mouth. "What age is she? Coming four?"

"I think she must be," said Christopher.

"Anybody'd think she'd be broken by now," went on
Ira, running his hand over her withers and down her
near-side foreleg. "Clean enough, isn't she?"

"Yes," I answered. "I fancy she'd make a nice driver
if she was put to it."

" I'll warrant she would," replied Ira, " and if you'll come along wi' me this morning, same as I asked you, I'll help you break her in. You can have my pony and trap to bring your *covels* [things] along, and then when we gets to a quiet old lane we'll put this 'un through her paces. What do you say, my brothers? "

" This," said Christopher. " We won't refuse what you ask, because one day, I hope not far from now, we will travel with you. There is nothing we'd like better, Mr Lovell, but just at the moment there are several reasons why we cannot."

" I understand," said Ira; " but give me your hand and make a pledge that you'll keep your word."

" What shall I pledge? " said Christopher.

" Say this," said Noah. " May the Devil take my breath if one day I don't go a-travelling with Ira Lovell! "

" May the Devil take my breath if I don't," said Christopher.

" Now," continued Ira, addressing me, " give me your hand and *pukka lesti* [tell it]."

These formalities having been exchanged, I asked Ira if a man in a green car had visited him during the morning.

" Yes," said Ira. " We had a hell of a paddy with him! He said that he was going to bring the *gavmush* [constable] to us. A proper *rye* [gentleman]—talks wi' a posh voice? "

" That's right," said I.

" Wears a green *stardie* [hat]," continued Ira. " Moves about summart like a cock bantam? "

" Yes," I said. " That would be Mr Crane. Did he tell you to shift? "

" Wanted us to fetch the horses and pull out while he was here," said the red-haired woman indignantly. " Said it was his lane! Why, I've stopped here since I can remember, so did my grandmother and also her grandmother."

" I told him to fetch the *muskero* [policeman] if he wanted us to shift, and he jumped up in his car and drove away," said Ira. " You had to shift, I suppose? "

" Yes, but of course we were on private ground."

" That does make a difference," remarked the red-haired woman thoughtfully.

" We heard your cousins leave this morning," said Christopher, after we had watched the peg-making for a few moments.

" You did," replied Ira. " They got up as soon as it was light. I made them a cup of tea, we harnessed the pony and off they went."

" I hope your brother gets on all right," said I, glancing at the wife, who had come out of the waggon with her baby. In daylight she hardly looked old enough to be the mother of the dark girl.

" I shan't worry so much, now that I know where he is," said the woman, speaking to us for the first time. " I hopes you both gets on better when you leaves here, for I can tell that you've had good and bad times, the same as us."

" Thank you," I said.

" God bless you both! " said the woman, moving her baby from one breast to the other.

Christopher, taking a brand from the fire and lighting a cigarette, said he thought it was time to be getting along.

Ira looked worried.

" I don't like to see you go with no better conveyance," said he. " Would you not like to make a chop for my pony and trap? "

" No," I said. " At the moment we can't offer you the difference."

" Listen to me! " went on Ira. " I likes you both and if I can help you I will. You haven't a lot of money, have you? "

" No," answered Christopher. " We haven't a lot of money."

" I didn't think you had, and so long as you go about like this, with not so much as an old trap and a bit of harness to go out and earn your living, you never will! I trusts you both and I'm going to let you take away my trap and pony with your own tied on behind. I want no money off you now. You can pay me when next we meets, and if you haven't got the money then, I shall not worry you. I've got plenty of money, and it's as safe doing you a bit of good as laying idle in the Savings Bank. There's the pony, there's the trap, and there's the harness. I value it at nine pounds ten shillings. And now I'll drive you to Warminster and back, for I could do with a drink and I'd like you to know I'm not pawning off anything on you."

" I shall always think a lot of what you have offered us," said Christopher, " but we wouldn't take the pony unless we had the money to pay for it."

" You need not feel like that," replied Ira. " You are

welcome to the pony and trap; but if I can't persuade you I want you to rest assured that you have a good friend in Ira Lovell. If ever you are in need, come to me and I'll give you whatever I have—God take my breath I will! Next time we meet, if my brother is back wi' us, we'll have a good time together. We'll go to the *livno-ker* [beer-house] and drink together, we'll have a step [step-dancing] and a good song; but if you can understand me, brother, to-day we feels *shillow ratted* [cold-blooded]."

" God Almighty bless you! " said the red-haired woman, leaving the pegs and shaking us warmly by the hand.

The dark girl stood up and with her face averted shook our hands.

" Good-bye," she murmured. " I hopes you have the best of luck."

The fair girl came forward, and when we had bidden her and all the children good-bye we took the pony by the bridle and started off down the lane to the gate, where we proposed cutting straight across the open downs.

✠ VIII ✠

THE SPOT WHICH MR CRANE HAD POINTED OUT PROVED
to be so boggy and gloomy that we decided to move on
until we reached a pleasanter stretch of country. The
ground was low-lying, the gorse bushes were of a shoddy
and stilted growth, and although from a distance the place
fitted in with the general plan of the down country it would
have made a dreary and depressing camping ground. Our
feet sank into the mire six or seven times, but at last we
reached a gate and began to ascend to a drier and more
wholesome soil. We passed through several rough grass
fields, grazed with sheep and cattle, and presently reached a
narrow downland valley, running between the slope on which
we stood and a ridge of wooded and more cultivated downs
before us. A Roman road, ploughed deep with wheel ruts,
ran through the centre of the valley, and to our left, beside
this track, lay the ruins of an old derelict small-holding.

A drizzling rain had begun to fall, and as the heavy clouds
indicated a wet afternoon we decided to make for the ruins
and enjoy our dinner under shelter.

It was a low two-roomed cottage, more like the hovels of
Ireland or Wales than anything I had seen before in Wiltshire. The walls were built with rough stone, the doorway
was in the middle and windows on either side. Once the
cottage had been divided into two rooms, but now the parti-

tion had collapsed, and what remained of the roof was covered with grass and moss. The most striking thing, however, was the great open fireplace built in one corner of the ruin. A big oak beam, at least eighteen inches square and ten feet long, supported the massive chimney. Above the fireplace and the hearth the roof was fairly intact and, except when a gust of wind blew the rain in, the corner remained dry and comfortable. I collected some of the wood that had fallen from the broken roof, and lit a fire in the grate. Christopher brought the pony inside, and having partly unloaded her we prepared some dinner and sat down in the corner beside the fire.

During the afternoon the rain became heavier, the wind rose, and at half-past three, when we walked to the window of the cottage, a drenching rain was blowing across the downs in gusts, sometimes so heavy that the sheep on the opposite hill were obscured from view.

" It's hardly worth moving to-day," I said, going to the doorway and looking at the dark clouds rolling one after another across the downs.

" No," replied Christopher, filling his pipe and returning to the hearth for a firebrand. " It's little use moving. But," he continued, puffing and retracing his steps to the window, " if the wind changes there'll be no shelter here."

" I don't think the wind'll change."

" Perhaps you're right," said Christopher. " If you'll find some wood, I'll get the hay. I should like to make a drawing before the light goes."

I collected three bundles of dry wood and sufficient straw to provide the pony and ourselves with a comfortable bed.

It took me some time to discover a dew-pond, which lay hidden in a hollow less than a mile from the cottage, but when at last I returned with a full kettle of water Christopher had unpacked the pony and was working on an interior drawing of the cottage. I made up the fire and put on the kettle, and when it grew too dark for my brother to work I made the tea and we settled down before the hearth.

We stuck three candles in the necks of some bottles left by last year's harvesters, the hurricane lamp was hung upon a beam, and, although the rain came in on one corner and the wind shrieked past the open windows and doorway, the place was comfortable and warm, and we thanked heaven that we were not shivering with cold among the stilted gorse bushes in Crane's bog.

During the evening the roof above the pony began creaking; as the gale increased we grew apprehensive of it collapsing and falling in on her.

" I think it would be as well to move her," I said.

" Where? " replied Christopher. " There are only two safe places in this ruin." He pointed to the corner by the fireplace, and to the corner where the rain poured in.

" We can't tie her up outside," I said, " on a night like this."

" I tell you what," said Christopher, knocking out his pipe and jumping up. " Alongside one of the straw ricks are several thick ash-poles, about twelve or fourteen feet long. If we cut one off at the right length we can prop it up against the beam."

" That's all very well," I said, " but if the pony knocks down the prop during the night, what then? "

" With a little care the prop could be wedged so securely that a full-grown cart-horse couldn't push it down."

I took down the hurricane lamp from the beam and we groped our way round to the ricks, where we found roughly the required length of prop. Between us we carried it back to the cottage, hacked off about nine inches with a chopper, and propped it up against the beam which supported the unsound portion of roof. This done, we ate supper, spread the straw out on the ground, and covered the beds with the tent sheet, lest the wind changed and drove in the rain. We gave the pony a good feed of hay and having secured her halter to a post which once supported the partition we undressed and went to bed. I did not feel disposed to read, but after turning out the hurricane lamp I lay awake for some time, listening to the wind and the rain moaning and shrieking over the stone tiles of the cottage. In spite of the fallen roof and the leaning walls I had seldom been more conscious of security and of the protection which the crumbling ruin afforded us against the fury of the storm.

I say ' had,' for since then I believe I have been even more aware of security. Oddly enough it was during one of the most precarious and insecure nights I have ever spent beyond the four walls of a sound house. It was during a terrific gale on the Yorkshire Wolds. We were travelling with our horse and caravan down the Yorkshire coast to Hull a few weeks before Christmas. The waggon weighed a ton and a half and our horse was as lively as an unbroken colt (the following spring she ran away and smashed up the waggon). Dusk was falling when we reached the foot of one of those long, steep hills that cross the Yorkshire Wolds.

We could not find a camping-place and we foolishly lit our lamps and began the ascent. A third of the way up the hill we turned directly into the wind, the road became steeper, and the horse fell after fighting for a grip on the smooth tar. We blocked up the waggon, the horse scrambled to its feet, and we began unloading all our possessions in the pouring rain—books, sacks of oats, chaff, coal tents, tent-poles, furniture, clothes and bedding. Then, with the help of a tramp, we wound the waggon from one side of the road to the other, until we were within a hundred yards of the summit of the Wolds. The treacherous gradient made it impossible for us to go on without further help, and the tramp, who wanted to reach Driffield before the lodging-houses closed, left us.

We stood in our saturated clothes, the rain pouring down our necks for twenty-five minutes, one at the horse's head, the other at the wheel-blocks. The wind roared past the waggon, which now was exposed to the full force of the gale, so that we expected to see it turn over at any moment. We had two alternatives. One was to wait for help, and the other was to turn back. We decided to wait for help, and at last a gang of labourers, returning from a stone quarry on the other side of the hill, appeared ahead. They were all powerfully built Yorkshiremen and without a word they put their shoulders to the waggon and heaved until we reached the extreme summit of the hill. We were determined not to go a yard farther than necessary—there was no grass verge to stay the night on the roadside—and we made straight for a gate leading into a ploughed field. It was locked.

" Then lift it off the hinges," said one of the Yorkshiremen.

I held a hurricane lamp over the gate and saw two heavy
iron stakes driven into the post above the hinges.

" I believe we have a hack-saw," Christopher said.

" Then cut the chain," replied a second Yorkshireman.
' The man who owns the ground is a miserable bastard.
It's the right way to serve him."

In a few minutes we cut a link out of the chain, and pulled
the waggon inside the field. The fire was already burning
in the range, and when the horse had been unharnessed and
fed we lit the lamps, changed our clothes, and ate a good
supper. Then we carried up the hill all the things which
we had unloaded on the roadside.

At eleven o'clock the gale increased and we were obliged
to rope the waggon down on the windward side. At twelve
o'clock we crawled into bed. Although the pegs were by
no means secure in the soft ploughed land and the waggon
rocked from side to side on its springs, I spent one of the
most restful nights in my life. I lay in the bunk listening to
the rain lashing against the waggon and watching the firelight flicker on the ceiling, and I was never so aware of my
security and of the comfort of my bed. Within a few
inches of my pillow the storm raged against the side of the
waggon. I was conscious and deeply grateful for the delicate
' penny-farthing ' boards with which the waggon was made;
I was conscious of the cheer and warmth of the fire, and
above all I was aware of the violence of the storm.

I was never, in reality, less secure. I often wonder what
kind of a night I should have spent had I known that the

ropes, which undoubtedly prevented the waggon from blowing over and being set alight, were frayed to the last strand; that the man who owned the field was mad, and was actually known to have discharged two barrels of a sporting gun at a young man and a girl who on a summer evening had driven their car just inside his gate and made love under one of his hedges.

☙ IX ☙

When I awoke in the morning the rain had stopped. There was, however, quite a strong north wind blowing and the sky was still overcast and cloudy. It was a quarter to seven, and as I busied myself lighting the fire and preparing breakfast a sudden shower of rain, lasting only a few minutes, beat on the roof.

I glanced at the clock. " Rain before seven, fine before eleven," I said to myself. I hung the kettle on the fire, and repeated the proverb. " It must have been made up," I said to myself, " long before the daylight-saving time was introduced. I wonder how many people in the summer wait until eight o'clock before they say whether it will be wet or fine at noon."

Soon after nine we loaded our things on the pony and left the ruined cottage. The Roman road, as I have said before, ran along the foot of the valley and, taking the direction which led farther into the downs, we walked steadily for close on four miles. The valley narrowed all the time and when it was little more than two hundred yards in width, the slopes rising abruptly on either side, we halted and surveyed the country. There were barns and sheds scattered on either side of the track behind us ; on the left, looking down the valley, the downs, which were dotted with gorse bushes and grazing sheep, rolled away into the distance. But it was the steep, rugged slope which ran up into a dense pine-wood on our right that attracted most of our attention.

" That's a fine place," I said, pointing to the edge of the wood which grew out on to a sharp point of land directly above us. " I should like to build our cottage among those trees on the edge of that plateau."

Christopher gazed upward. " I think," he said, " it would be as well to camp there now."

We opened a gate which led out of the lane, and after filling the kettle at a trough began the ascent up into the wood. The slope soon became so steep that we had to zig-zag the pony from side to side. On two occasions the load slipped and fell to the ground so that the pony could not move one leg in front of the other. The first time this happened we were able to straighten it with little difficulty, but on the second occasion the pony was struggling to gain altitude as she turned for another climb. The load slipped and swung like a pendulum under her belly, but in spite of the mishap she was determined to make another two or three feet, and though we did our best to stop her she struggled on until she collapsed on the ground. We were only just in time to prevent her from rolling like a ball down the hill. She put both front feet through the tent sheet, and the difficulty we had in stripping off the baggage and removing the tent before it was ruined was incredible. When at last we reached the top we made our way through the wood to the trees which grew on the protruding jut of land and as we stood looking down into the valley, which because of the abrupt rise of the land seemed a great way below, our memories of the hill of the gorse bushes became faint and insignificant.

We unloaded the pony and put up the tent amid the foremost pine-trees. In the wood directly behind us there were numbers of either dying or dead fir- and pine-trees and we spent the afternoon strolling round with a chopper, marking and measuring all the trees which we thought would be suitable for our building material.

It grew dark and we collected a great heap of dry firewood and stacked it beside the tent. The wind had dropped during the afternoon, the clouds now gradually cleared away, and by half-past eight in the evening a bright moon appeared and shone down through the pine-trees, casting strange lights and shadows in the wood around our camp.

I walked down to the foot of the hill and filled the kettle at the trough. When I retraced my steps up the hillside and came into view of the camp, I was impressed by an almost Canadian atmosphere made by the fire, the tent, and the pony, against the background of pine-trees. An owl flew on to the top branch of a tree directly above the camp, and hooted gloomily until I went to sleep.

There was a sharp frost in the night, and in the morning when we got up the pony's mane and tail were covered in silvery frost and the water in the kettle frozen an inch thick. As I collected wood for breakfast the grass crunched under my feet like frozen snow, and my hands were so cold that I could hardly strike a match to kindle the fire.

" I think," said Christopher, as he fried the breakfast over the blazing sticks, " we'd better walk to the nearest village this morning and find out who owns this wood."

" God forbid it's a gentleman farmer," I said, rolling a cigarette.

" It might belong to some one worse," replied Christopher.

" I'm convinced that there is no one worse," I answered, licking the cigarette paper and turning down the edge.

Christopher held up a finger.

" Listen ! " he said with a look of melancholy disapproval.

I listened, and above the wood I heard a pheasant launch itself into the air and, as it performed its awkward, hurried flight, utter its shrill and equally awkward cry.

" There are country gentlemen," he continued, looking fixedly at me.

We caught the pony and made our way down the lane, and after passing the ruined cottage and walking for another two miles we reached the edge of the downs. A village of farms and cottages lay to our left, midway on the slopes of the downs; and, expecting the landowner to live beneath one of its thatched roofs, we branched off down a narrow, muddy lane which led us into the village. The public-house, which seemed the most sensible place to gather a little first-hand information, was, oddly enough, the nearest building to the mouth of the lane. It was a pleasant-looking inn, very plain and typical of Wiltshire. An immense hanger bearing the nocturnal sign of a half-moon stood by the roadside, and in front of the inn itself was a yard, enclosed on either side by stables and out-buildings.

I tied the pony up and followed Christopher into the bar. A bright log fire was burning in the grate and, considering that it was a weekday morning and that the inn was several miles from the main road, I thought the place was surprisingly full. Christopher ordered two pints of beer, and we walked over to the fire and sat down in two empty chairs. When we had opened the door an old man, seated directly in front of the fire, had been entertaining the men in the bar, and now that we were seated every one's attention reverted to him. He was a large man, his face was red and his nose was very purple. A worn trilby hat rested upon the back of his head and several ragged overcoats upon his back. His trousers were tied with string about the knees; and in his hand he held a pint mug of rough cider. While I was watching the big man I suddenly observed a white furry head emerge from one of his inside pockets. Two bright pink eyes looked rapidly round the bar, and a moment later a full-grown polecat crawled out of the pocket and ran up the old man's arm. I was just about to express my astonishment when I observed that no one took any notice of the animal and that its owner made no attempt to catch it.

Presently the big man rose, not without difficulty, and staggering to the bar ordered his mug to be replenished. When he returned he sat down heavily in his chair and looked at us.

" Excuse me," he said at last. " Are you strangers? "

" Yes," said I, " we are."

" Oh (hic), I daresay you are on the roads? "

" More or less."

" You know, I'm very well acquainted with the roads myself."

" You are? " said I. " I——"

" Yes," he continued, " I expect I know the roads better than you."

"I wouldn't be surprised," said Christopher. "You've lived longer."

"The Devil!" exclaimed the old man suddenly. "You are speaking to old Scout (hic). I'm of, what you might say, a very congenial disposition (hic). Will you have a drink with me?"

"Thank you," said Christopher.

We emptied our glasses and when Scout had paid for them to be refilled he looked at us as if to say: "Now perhaps you'll tell me summat?"

Christopher sketched our movements and asked who owned the land on which we were camping.

"Why, it's the bloke I'm working for!" said the big man. "Farmer Steele. I'm supposed to be catching his rabbits—been working for him this five weeks."

"He pays you by the amount you catch," I suggested.

"No, no, regular hours. 'Course, it wouldn't do for him to see me sitting here, but on the whole he's a very good boss. I've no complaints to make against him, and you see I'm only in here nights and mornings."

"You live in the village?" I asked.

"No!" said Scout. "I don't live anywhere regular. There is an old shed just outside the village where I often sleep, but if I put in me hours after closing-time I sleep where I can."

"You've no home anywhere, then?"

"Lord, no! If it wasn't for these blooming things," said he, pointing to the polecats, "I should be quite independent."

"They don't seem to be a great tie." I asked him whether

he thought Mr Steele was the sort of man who would rent us a piece of ground. " I don't know if you've ever come across a farmer by the name of Crane," I continued. " He lives near here."

" Crane," repeated old Scout. " Yes, I worked for him once. He was always a-following of me round. One afternoon he found me asleep under a hedge. ' I thought I paid you to work? ' he says. ' You are dismissed! '—' Dismissed! ' said I. ' I'm sorry for that, 'cos I should like you to have paid me to flatten that helevated nose of yours ! ' "

" He wouldn't rent us any of his ground," I said. " Would you say that Mr Steele is a different kind of man? "

" As different as chalk from cheese."

I hopefully collected the mugs and ordered another round of drinks and a plate of bread and cheese. During the preceding conversation a second polecat had emerged from one of the many pockets of the big man. It had climbed on to his shoulder and for some time it had been sitting cleaning itself. I watched the little animal while the beer was being drawn. It finished washing, stood upon its haunches, looked about, scented the air, and crawled across Joe's back to his left shoulder. If I had been more used to polecats I probably should have discovered its intentions in time to warn Scout, but it was not until the old man with a shout put his hand to his neck, and an overwhelming stench of a polecat met my nostrils, that I realized what had happened.

" Hell and damnation on you ! " cried the old man, seizing the animal and shaking it furiously. " That's the third time you've done that this marning ! "

The polecats were savagely returned to their pockets and old Scout was shown round to the pump at the back door. When he returned and the laughter had died down, we finished our beer and our bread and cheese.

Scout picked up his empty mug.

" We'd better have another before we go on," he said.

" Yes," I replied. " It's a bit raw outside."

" And we'd better have a couple of bottles to take away," said Scout, five minutes later, " (hic) hadn't we? "

" All right," Christopher replied. " We'll have two or three."

" Landlord," said Scout, " would you be so kind as to bottle three pints of draught beer? " He turned to us : " I can't stick that there bottled stuff."

Outside we untied the pony, and Scout, having offered to accompany us on to the downs, where he had earlier set some rabbit wires, waited while we walked to the village shop. We decided to postpone our visit to Mr Steele. Beside some sheds in a hollow just below the top we sat down on the grass bank and passed the bottle round.

" A good thing we thought of bringing a drop," said the big man, sinking heavily to the ground. " I was beginning to get a bit dry."

When we had emptied the first bottle we were disturbed by the sound of a galloping horse. I stood up and saw a young man, mounted on a fine grey horse, descending from the downs.

" Who is it? " said Scout, handing the second bottle to Christopher and laying himself flat out on the grass.

" It's a young man on a fine grey horse," I said.

" Good God ! " cried Scout, lurching himself into a sitting position. " That's the governor's son ! "

" You think it is? "

" Yes ! Quick, hide those bottles ! He'll think we're having a picnic or summat ! " The big man scrambled to his feet and when the bottles were hidden I opened the gate adjoining the sheds.

" Good morning," I said, when the young man had reined in his horse with some difficulty.

" Good morning," he answered, half smiling. " Are you the people from the camp up in the wood? "

" Yes," answered Christopher. " I believe it is your land? "

" Yes—at least, it's my father's."

" I hope you don't mind? " said Christopher.

The young man looked a little amused.

" As a matter of fact, I have been riding round the place for more than an hour. I thought you were hiding in the wood or up in the trees."

" To tell you the truth," said Christopher, " we were coming to see you to-morrow. We want to try and rent the piece of ground where we are camping. I am a painter, my brother writes, and we are looking for a wild spot in which to build a shack."

" I can't promise anything," he answered, " but I'll certainly ask my father."

" Thank you," said Christopher. " Shall we walk down to the farm to-night? "

" No, I'll bring him up to see you. We ride over the

downs to look at the sheep every morning at about ten o'clock."

When the horse disappeared we emptied the last bottle and hid it in the hedge, and promising to meet old Scout the next day we left him to attend to his wires. The field where the snares were set was extremely steep, and the old man, having crawled up the rungs of the gate, landed flat on his back on the other side. He collected himself with difficulty and started off along the top hedge with a staggering gait; when he came near a wire he threw out both his hands and groped wildly for it, until one of his feet or his hands became entangled and dragged him heavily to earth. But the trouble did not really begin until he reached the end of the top hedge and started to go downhill.

The gradient was exceedingly steep, and Scout hardly descended a couple of yards before his stagger grew alarmingly fast. He checked himself in the nick of time by a young ash-tree, which he grabbed and uprooted. But it was not the danger that had made Scout stop, for no sooner had he landed on his back, the uprooted ash-tree clutched in his hands, than he crawled up the hedge to a snare which he had passed. Once more the great bulk rose upright, swayed, tottered, and careered down the hillside. I shall never forget the sight of Scout's short legs tearing faster and faster in a vain effort to keep pace with the vast body sweeping majestically ahead. It was a race between Scout's legs and Scout's helpless body. Sometimes, when the angle was less acute, it seemed that Scout's legs had a chance of winning, but from the start we knew that a disaster was inevitable. Gradually his head and shoulders gained until his legs were literally running behind. Then suddenly his hands spread out. He seemed for a moment to lift bodily into the air, then he plunged almost gracefully into the hedge which ran along the bottom of the fields.

"I expect," said Christopher, "he will stay there for the rest of the afternoon."

No movement came from Scout, but feeling instinctively that he was not hurt we took Sally by the bridle, called Nell to heel, and made our way back to the camp.

After we had eaten our dinner Christopher lit a cigarette and looked at me.

"I am afraid old Scout is going to be a bad influence."

"Yes," I replied. "If we stay here we'll have to be very firm with him."

"On no account must we go down to the village again to-night."

"No," I said, "we'll sit by the fire and listen to the owls and peewits."

"And tell sad stories of the death of kings," added my brother, breaking up some wood and throwing it on the fire.

❧ X ❧

I WAS DISTURBED IN THE MIDDLE OF THE NIGHT BY THE flapping of the canvas, and raising my head I looked out of the tent and saw that a storm was springing up. The moon was directly in front of the tent, and as I lay in bed I watched the small, dark clouds scurrying across the sky, as if they were the outriders of the coming storm. Faster, bigger, and darker they grew until the moon was only visible for short intervals, and the sky an inferno of twisting and turning cloud, sometimes of a silvery brilliance and the next moment a foreboding black.

A few moments before the rain began the pony, tethered to a tree near the camp, stopped eating, whinnied and stood with her head erect as if listening for a distant reply. On the other side of the valley I heard the faint neigh of another horse, and Sally, turning her back to the wind, went on grazing. It is strange how at night horses will neigh to one another before a storm.

With a violent gust of wind which shook the tent the rain came and beat down through the pine-trees on to the roof. I turned over and was just about to go to sleep again when I noticed the tear which the pony had made when she put her feet through the tent. I lit a candle. The rain was coming in fast and I awakened my brother, who helped me mend the tear with a piece of wire and several old safety-pins.

In the morning the storm had increased rather than abated. The wind was cold and so strong that we had great difficulty in preventing the fire from being blown away. At last, rather than eat our breakfast in such discomfort we borrowed two blankets from our bed and erected a shelter round the fireplace. The smoke was inclined to blow into our eyes, but we managed to eat a good breakfast and at ten o'clock we were looking out for the arrival of Mr Steele and his son. Soon I heard the sound of approaching horses and looking through the trees I saw the young farmer on his grey half-Arab and an older man, whom I presumed to be Mr Steele himself, on a thickset black horse. When the two men reached the camp they wished us good morning, and the farmer, leaning on the withers of his horse, said:

" My son has been telling me that you want to build a hut up here."

" Yes," I said. " We're hoping that you'll be able to rent us a piece of ground."

The farmer took his left foot out of its stirrup and scratched his ankle. " I'm afraid that the land does not belong to me. I rent it, up to the edge of this wood, from Colonel Sage. He lives at E— Manor."

Christopher glanced at me rather despairingly. " Do you think," he said, " he would let us build a place here? "

" It's impossible for me to say," replied Mr Steele. " Would you like me to ring him up this afternoon and put in a good word for you? I believe he's at home this week."

" Thank you," said Christopher. " Perhaps you could

arrange for us to see him? Is he a good-natured sort of man?"

"Yes, I think so. He is supposed to be fond of painting. More than likely he will take an interest in you." The farmer looked curiously at our camp and the screen of blankets round the fire, and asked if we did not find it very cold living outside in the winter.

"It's quite comfortable," replied Christopher, "so long as we can get plenty of firewood."

"You must be used to it," said Mr Steele. "In the middle of winter it's strange to see two young fellows living outside with a stick tent and a pony."

"We never stay under a roof for long either in the winter or the summer," I said.

"Did your parents travel about like this?"

"A good deal," Christopher answered. "My father often travelled about with horses and tents. He was a playwright."

"You are English, I suppose?"

"We're natives of this county," I said. "We were born near Marlborough."

In the conversation that followed we discovered that the farmer was born in the same village. We discussed historical details of Aldbourne, the village pond and its ' dab-chicks,' and presently he asked whether we knew the origin of the Wiltshire ' Moon Rakers.'

"I've always understood that the story was founded on the supposed simplicity of Wiltshire men," I said.

"Most people believe that," replied Mr Steele. "The story is true, but it does not originate from the Wiltshire

man's simplicity. You remember how a constable was supposed to have found a crowd of men raking a pond on a
moonlight night, and when he asked what they were doing
they pointed to the reflection of the moon and said: 'We
be raking for that there great lump of cheese.' "

" I always thought that was as far as the story went."

" No, it's where the story begins," continued the farmer.
" It was in the days of smugglers, and the pond was used
to hide the goods that the smugglers sold the natives. The
Wiltshire men were dragging the stuff out of the pond
with long rakes, and when the constable or exciseman came
along they gravely raked at the reflection of the moon,
and said: 'We be raking for that there great lump of
cheese.' "

We talked for an hour or more with the farmer and his
son, and when they rode away we returned to the fire and
discussed the possibilities of a successful arrangement with
Colonel Sage. The fact that he was interested in painting
and letters afforded us some consolation, but every time a
pheasant flew overhead, or shrieked from the depth of the
wood, we started and glanced up uneasily.

During the day the wind and the rain became stronger
and colder. The shelter which we had erected round the
fire in the morning became inadequate, and one by one we
removed the rest of the blankets until the fire was completely enclosed and the smoke drew almost straight up.
At five o'clock, when I was sitting beside the fire waiting
for the kettle to boil for tea I heard my brother, who had
been away for some time, returning through the wood.
The shuffle of his footsteps indicated that he was walking

under a heavy burden, and standing up I looked over the top of the shelter and saw him approaching with a dead or dying animal in his arms.

" What on earth have you got there? " I said, pulling back the shelter for him to enter. " Is it alive? "

" Yes," replied Christopher, crawling in and laying an almost lifeless ewe beside the fire. " She must have been on her back for days."

" Where did you find her? " said I, feeling the protruding ribs.

" In a hollow in the middle of the wood. The fir-trees are so thick that I had to crawl under the branches."

" I should think she's been lying in the water," I said, feeling the saturated wool.

I fetched some dry hay from the tent and we put the animal beside the fire. Then, after heating some milk and feeding the ewe with a small bottle, I brewed the tea and we sat down beside the fire.

" Don't you think we ought to find the shepherd? " I said, when we had finished eating.

" There are two cottages at the back of the wood, about a mile and a half from here," said Christopher. " I was thinking that most likely he lives there."

When we had washed up the tea-things I left Christopher to look after the fire and walked round the wood. In time I saw the lights of the cottages. Knocking at the door of the first cottage I was confronted by a young labourer.

" I'm looking for Mr Steele's shepherd," I said.

" He lives down in the village," said the man, holding up a hurricane lamp.

I returned to the camp; we doused the fire, and started down to the village with the pony and the dog. We passed through the gate at the bottom of the descent, but had scarcely gone a mile down the lane when we saw a dim light swaying from side to side and moving slowly towards us.

" I wonder who that is? " said Christopher.

" Some one lost or drunk."

" Hush! " said Christopher, suddenly stopping. " I believe I heard a voice. Yes, there it is again! "

I listened and presently I heard the sound of a woman's voice. We stood quite still and as the light swayed towards us the voice grew more distinct. At frequent intervals the woman, whoever she was, cried out loudly, but it was neither the fact that she was a woman nor the fact that she shouted which caused us such astonishment.

I looked at my brother. " Am I dreaming? "

" If you are," he said without removing his gaze from the swaying lamp, " I am. What would you say she's crying? "

" Fish! " I exclaimed.

" Undoubtedly! " replied my brother.

The woman was now within three hundred yards of us. " Fish! Fish! Fish! " she shouted, as she swung the lamp to and fro. " Fish! Fish! Fish! "

" I can't understand it," I said. " No one sane would try to sell fish at this time of night on these downs! "

" Fish! " yelled the woman insistently.

" Let's go on," said Christopher. " Mad or not, if she finds us standing here with the pony she'll be frightened to death."

We walked on, and in a few minutes were able to distinguish the woman by the light of the hurricane lamp which she was carrying. She looked about sixty-five or seventy years old, a bonnet covered her head, and as she gazed across the downs on her right she held up the lamp at arm's length.

"Fish! Fish! Fish!" she continued to cry in an unvaried voice, without taking the slightest heed of us.

"I am afraid she'll walk right into us," whispered Christopher when she was almost upon the pony.

On she came, and although we made as much noise as possible she continued walking until suddenly she came face to face with Sally.

"Fish!" she cried. "Fi—— Oh, my God!"

"It's all right," I said hastily, "don't be alarmed."

"Oh, my dear God!" she gasped, thrusting the lamp up to our faces. "Oh, how you frightened me!"

"We tried to make you hear," shouted Christopher. He took it for granted that she was deaf. "We're on our way to the village."

"I really didn't expect to meet anyone up here to-night," she said with an uncertain smile.

"I should rather have thought you did," said Christopher, recalling the impression that her cries had first made on us.

"Gracious, no," exclaimed the old woman with dreadful seriousness. "I've lost my mistress's little dog."

"A dog!" repeated Christopher.

"Yes, poor little thing," muttered the old woman. "What my mistress will say when she gets back, only God Almighty knows!"

" What does the dog look like? " I managed to ask.

" It's a Yorkshire terrier with a soft, fluffy, brown coat," she replied. " If you should see him, call ' Fish! Fish! ' I live at the doctor's house in the village. Ask for Sarah Rose."

" We will," I said. " I do hope you'll find him."

" Thank you kindly," replied the old woman, and after saying good night she continued her way up the lane. The light disappeared behind a hill and the plaintive cry of " Fish! Fish! Fish! " grew fainter and fainter, until it could no longer be heard.

✄ XI ✄

On reaching the village we inquired for the shepherd's house, which we found on the outskirts. The door was opened by a dark young man.

" Are you Mr Steele's shepherd? " Christopher asked.

" I am," answered the young man, holding the door back so that the light of the room fell on our faces.

" I found a ewe in the wood where we're camping. She's been on her back for several days, and I wondered if you would come up and look at her in the morning? "

The shepherd asked us to explain where we were camping. " Step inside," he said. " The wife is bathing the little girl and there's a hell of a draught with the door open."

We went inside and found ourselves in a big kitchen. A young woman was kneeling on the hearth bathing a little girl of about seven years. In the middle of the room stood a massive deal kitchen table, at which sat two smaller children, busy cutting pictures out of a pile of magazines and papers that lay scattered around the oil lamp.

Christopher asked for a piece of paper and pencil, and when he had explained the position of our camp I invited the shepherd to accompany us to the Half Moon.

" Thank you, but I've been to Warminster with the wife to-day," he replied. " I cannot afford it on a week night or after I've been to town. It costs summat to look after all these youngerns."

I looked at the plump, sturdy little children and thought of the struggle it must be to live and feed their hungry bellies on his wages.

"I'd have a couple of pints every night if I had the money," he continued. "My grandfather never touched anything but beer all his life. He had it for breakfast, dinner, tea, and supper, and I'll warrant you never saw a healthier old man in your life."

"I don't disbelieve you," I said. "It's a great mistake taxing beer beyond the working man's pocket. It's a food a land-worker needs."

"It's a thousand pities," said the shepherd, "a few of the prattling old fools who say that beer isn't a necessity to the working man hadn't lived in the days when a man scythed an acre of grass before breakfast. A good mower would drink a gallon of beer before eight o'clock in the morning and a good farmer wouldn't begrudge him a cup full of it."

"I often wonder if a farm-worker is any better off since the War," said Christopher as he offered the shepherd a cigarette.

"Well, yes and no," replied the shepherd. "Years ago he had little money, but he had a lot of advantages which I think were worth more than his money to-day."

"What advantages?" I asked. "Or rather what are the present disadvantages?"

"Well, do you know that Mr Steele is the only man around here who allows his men to keep pigs and chicken?

The bastards are all afraid the men will steal a bit of meal or maize."

" Which they used to be given," I put in.

" Yes," continued the shepherd. " What they used to be given. To-day the labourer pays rent for his cottage. Years ago he was always given a cottage and a garden. We eat three loaves a day, seven and fivepence a week. Before the binding machines came into use the women and the children went out gleaning. When I was a little 'un my mother and my brothers and sisters gleaned enough grain every harvest to last three-quarters of the year."

" And how did you get it thrashed and milled? "

" The farmers had a special day to thrash the labourer's gleanings. Later he lent a horse and a waggon to take the grain to the mills. In those days money was worth double what it is to-day."

" That's true," I said. " I believe the depreciation since the War is over forty per cent. But wouldn't it now pay to buy the flour and bake the bread? "

" No," said the shepherd. " The wife often bakes, but it only saves about a farthing a loaf. The tax is not on baking. Milk is another expense. It would surprise some people to know how many farm-labourers' children are brought up on tinned milk. Years ago it was an unwritten law that every farmer allowed his men as much milk as their families required. To-day butter is made in the big dairies, and if we can't afford the shop price we have to eat margarine."

" Now what would you say were the things against those days? " I asked.

" The slavery," replied the shepherd. " The power the master had over his men. I don't know whether I can find it, but if I can I'll show you summat that I think will interest you."

The shepherd went to a cupboard and began rummaging about among a heap of old papers and oddments, while the woman, having wrapped the curly-headed girl in a blanket and left her squealing with delight on the hearth, cleared the table and began laying the supper.

" Kate, where is that old form? " said the shepherd.

" I haven't set eyes on it for years," answered his wife.

" A pity," he said, closing the cupboard door. " I should like them to have seen it."

" What was it? " I asked.

" An old form used for hiring farm-labourers during the times of which we've been talking. Will you come back and have a bit of supper with us? It'll not be out of your way."

We accepted the invitation, and when we left the cottage we untied the pony from the garden gate and made our way along the road until we came to the sign of the Half Moon. The big man was in the bar, and when we entered he sprang up and gave us a warm welcome.

" I've been waiting here all day," he said. " In another minute I should have gone up on to the downs to see what had become of you."

The old man ordered two pints of beer and we sat down with him beside the fire.

" How did you get on yesterday afternoon? " I asked.

" I woke up at six o'clock and found myself under a hedge. It took me nearly all night to catch the ferrets."

When our tankards were empty I ordered a second round, but, remembering the shepherd's invitation and wishing to avoid a recurrence of yesterday's drunkenness, I ordered half-pints. Old Scout, however, was up in arms at the mere suggestion of such niggardliness and, evidently thinking that the reform had been caused by a shortage of money, slammed two shillings on the table and commanded the landlord on his life to serve us with two pints of beer. The clock fortunately struck ten and time was called before old Scout had the opportunity of making us too drunk to eat supper with the shepherd, but on leaving the inn a new difficulty arose. The old man said that he would return to the camp and spend the night with us, and when Scout made up his mind about anything it was no easy matter to change it.

" *Keker, lesti's borie* to *sove adray* the *tikno tan!* [No, he's too big to lie in the little tent]," I whispered to Christopher.

I visualized him sleeping in our tent, the canvas heaving up and down as he breathed, his hobnailed boots sticking out at the front, while we in an effort to keep warm paced solemnly up and down or crawled in on either side of him like chicks under their mother's wing.

" *Awal, cur lesti sove adray* the *granza* [Yes, make him sleep in the barn]," returned Christopher.

We escorted Scout to the barn, in which, he had previously told us, he often slept. It was an immense thatched building which, I should think, was originally constructed so that a thrashing-machine might be operated inside. The whole structure was made of hard wood, the elm boards which covered the sides were overlapped one upon another, and the oak beams supporting the roof were arranged in the usual design of the old Wiltshire grain barns. It was evidently customary for Scout to crawl under the great doors when he entered, but fearing to release him until we were safely inside Christopher crept in and drew back the bolts. When the three of us were in I shut the doors and we sat down on a heap of dry straw in a corner of the barn. We had brought two or three bottles of beer to drink with the shepherd, but, anxious to get Scout to sleep as soon as possible, I opened one bottle and to the best of my ability poured the contents down his throat.

" Aren't we going back to your place? " he said, when he had finished the beer.

" Too far," said Christopher.

" Too far? "

" Yes," said I softly, " too far."

Scout settled himself down in the straw and his eyes closed.

" Too far," he muttered contentedly, " much too far."

We waited until he was properly asleep, then crept across the barn and crawled under the great doors.

Coaxing the pony into a trot we hurried back to the shepherd's house. We were glad to find a light still burning in the kitchen and the shepherd and his wife waiting to begin supper. I apologized for our delay and placed the beer and the stout on the table. The woman cut the bread, the shepherd the cheese, and helping ourselves to butter and several excellent home-grown shallots we ate an enjoyable meal.

"I hope your wife likes stout," I said to the shepherd, observing that the bottles remained untouched.

"Yes, I generally bring her back a drop of stout when I go to the public."

"Good," said I, opening the bottles and filling the mugs which the young woman then provided.

Christopher passed his tobacco to the shepherd, and when we had all drunk and lit our pipes and cigarettes I asked if the old hiring-form had been found.

"Yes, I have it here," answered the shepherd, going to the mantelpiece and taking down a small slip of blue paper. "You'll now understand what I mean by slavery."

I took the paper in my hand and holding it up to the oil lamp read as follows:

Frederick Rose of the Parish of Ogbourn in the County of *Wiltshire* hereby hires himself from the eleventh of October instant, for twelve calendar months now next ensuing, to serve Mr —— at ——*Farm*, in the Parish of *Heytesbury* in the County of *Wiltshire* as *carter* to receive weekly, while actually labouring, the sum of £— *11s.* —*d.* and, on the completion of his year's service, the further sum of £2; one-third of which additional amount shall be due for extra labour in the Hay Harvest; and the balance of the remaining two-thirds, for the additional labour of the Corn Harvest.

The said *Frederick Rose* hereby undertakes to make himself generally useful in all he may be required to do in the Agricultural pursuits of the farm; to regularly attend a Place

138

of Worship at least once on every Sabbath, and to be at home always every night during the winter half-year at *eight* o'clock, and during the summer half-year at *ten* o'clock, unless the business of the Farm, or anything else of a special nature, which would receive the sanction of his master, should prevent it.

(Signed)   X

At *Warminster Fair* this *11th* day of *October*, 1860.

Witness.............

"I would hardly believe it if it wasn't in black and white!" I said, handing the form to Christopher when I had finished. "May I copy it before we leave?"

"I'll fetch you a paper and pencil," replied the shepherd.

When my brother had finished reading I copied the form carefully and handed it back to the shepherd.

"You are quite right," I said. "A labourer could have been no better off than a slave."

"True. But I think it is nearly as bad to stop a man keeping fowls and pigs in his own home. To-day a master does not give his men a chance to thieve, but seeing how this new order of things suits only the master's pocket I doubt whether the new way of saving his men's souls from hell is any better than the old."

"There's a lot in that," said Christopher as he picked up the hiring-form and turned to the shepherd.

"Warminster Fair?" he said. "I suppose the local farmers went there and hired labourers?"

"Not always. There were fairs in all the big villages during the fall of the year. A shepherd wore a piece of wool in his hat, a cowman a piece of horsehair, and a carter a piece of whipcord."

Before we left the cottage the shepherd told us of a short cut back to the encampment. He said that it would be a drier walk and save two miles, so having said good night we took the lane directed and made our way up to the downs. The storm had cleared during the evening, but it was a pitch-dark night and, after the light in the shepherd's cottage, it was difficult to see more than a few yards ahead. When we reached the summit of the downs the lane widened out into a hard, grass, fenced-in trackway, which kept a straight, undulating course for about a mile and three-quarters. We walked along at a comfortable pace, smoking and talking, until we suddenly came to a fork at which the lane divided and branched off in two different directions.

" The shepherd said nothing of this," I said, stopping and not knowing which way to turn.

" No," replied Christopher. " And we'll have nothing to guide us until the moon rises."

" What time'll that be ? " I said, trying to recollect when I had seen the moon the previous evening.

" After midnight. We'll risk it and take the turning to the left."

Once more we started off, but we had scarcely walked half a mile when we found ourselves standing on a crossing of five roads, each of which turned off at such an irrelevant angle that it was impossible to choose a track opposite to the one on which we approached. I had an ordnance map in my overcoat pocket and kneeling down I spread it out on the ground and lit a match. The first match lasted just long enough for me to find Warminster; with the second I managed to locate Heytesbury; with the third the village and the Half Moon; with the fourth the lane; with the fifth the fork roads. The sixth match was blown out, the seventh—confound it! I had lost the place.

"Stop!" yelled Christopher. "Those are the only blasted matches we have."

I hastily felt inside the box.

"Surely you have some," I protested. "There is only one here."

"Then for God's sake keep it for lighting a fire," answered my brother irritably.

We took the widest of the two lanes opposite us and walked in silence until we reached a stone shed which stood alone on the bleak downs.

"We had better lie here until daylight," I said, stopping outside the shed.

"Until the moon is up, at any rate," answered Christopher.

The barn was open at the bottom, and tying up the pony in reach of some straw I followed Christopher up a ladder into the loft, where we lay down and quickly fell asleep.

⚒ XII ⚒

I COULD NOT HAVE BEEN ASLEEP MORE THAN HALF AN HOUR when I woke up and found my brother missing. The place seemed lighter, and raising my head off the straw I saw that the loft doors were open and that Christopher was standing in front of them looking out across the downs.

" What's the matter? " I said sleepily.

He turned round.

" Whereabouts do you expect the moon to rise? " he asked.

" To the right."

" So do I."

I jumped up and looked out of the loft doors. On what I thought was the western horizon I saw a brilliant glare of deep yellow light.

" That can't be the moon."

" It must be," replied Christopher. " The sun won't be up for another five and a half hours."

" I should say that it was some ricks on fire."

" No, it's a clear night and the moon should be coming up now."

We watched, and as the light on the horizon spread and grew brighter the moon appeared and slowly rose like a great sphere of fire.

"I've never seen the moon look so big or of so deep a red colour," I said.

"Nor I," said Christopher. "It is more like a sunset."

A delicate line of cloud hung over the horizon like a drift of fine mist, and as the moon rose higher into the heavens the redness died away and a brilliant cold light was cast over the earth.

"Look!" said Christopher, suddenly pointing across the downs below us. "I believe that is the clump of trees above our wood."

We climbed down from the loft and, releasing the pony, started off towards the clump of trees. The moon had now mounted high and it was possible to distinguish landmarks and the general lie of the country with little difficulty. We reached the clump and looking down we saw the wood stretching out below us. The trees above the camp were almost visible and in less than a quarter of an hour we were back in the camp. The slight breeze which had been blowing during the evening had dried the blankets, and while I made the beds Christopher lit a small fire and fed the ewe.

In spite of the late hour at which we went to bed we awaited news from Colonel Sage with such eagerness that I was up and preparing breakfast soon after the sun had risen. At ten o'clock the farmer and his son appeared on their horses. They had seen the shepherd, who had told them about the ewe, and they dismounted and with our assistance drenched the animal.

"If I leave this bottle will you look after her while you are here?" asked the farmer.

I took the medicine and put it in the back of the tent.

" I rang up Colonel Sage yesterday," I heard the farmer say. " He told me to send you along this afternoon."

" Did he seem amiable? " I asked as I came out of the tent.

" He always does," replied the farmer.

We talked for some time, and when the horsemen disappeared through the trees we brought out the razor and, unable to find the looking-glass, hacked at one another's beards.

It was a quarter to three on a damp, depressing afternoon when, walking along the road from the village to S——, we came in sight of the great wrought-iron gates at the entrance to Colonel Sage's main drive.

" Very impressive," said I, looking up at the gilt spikes standing at least fifteen feet above us.

" A little overpowering to foot passengers," Christopher grunted.

" Then why not both sit on the pony," I retorted, " and make a more stately arrival? "

" No," replied Christopher, who seemed pessimistic. " She might jib before the manor-house."

A hundred yards down the road we found a secluded field and, after tying the dog and the pony to the hedge, we returned to the gates and made our way up the drive to the great house. As we approached we heard voices and laughter, and on turning into the main courtyard we found several cars preparing to move off. A man of between fifty and sixty years, whom we took to be the Colonel, stood on the steps below the front door talking with the departing guests.

WILTSHIRE FARM

By the time we reached the house the conventional exchange of humour was over, and the people, shrieking with equally conventional laughter, swept away in their cars. The Colonel then caught sight of us, held out both his hands, and coming forward gave us a warm welcome.

" You're the courageous young men, I believe, who are camping on my land," said he, smiling and shaking us by the hand.

" Yes," answered Christopher. " And you are Colonel Sage."

" Quite correct," answered the great man. " Come in, come in. You know I'm delighted to have you on my ground; I believe you are both charming young men. Steele told me about you."

He escorted us into an elegant hall, hung with ancestral portraits, firearms, and leopard-skins.

" Which of you is the painter? " he continued, opening a door and leading us into a wide, oak-panelled smoking-room. The ceiling of the room was deeply inlaid and over a magnificent seventeenth-century fireplace was the family coat-of-arms.

I am," answered Christopher, glancing at the paintings on the walls.

The Colonel drew up some chairs and the three of us sat down at a round oak table in the centre of the room.

" My sister, Lady ——, has a portrait by your uncle," he said, passing round a box of cigars. " Are you a landscape or portrait painter? "

" Both," answered Christopher, helping himself to a cigar. " I always think portrait or landscape painting on their own are just professions. An artist should be able to paint everything."

"I quite agree," said the Colonel. "Now tell me, do you write poetry or prose?"

"Chiefly prose," I said. "For an author I hardly think it's necessary to write both."

Our host smiled.

"I think you're right," said he. "Between poetry and prose there is as great a distinction as between sculpture and painting; only exceptions like Leonardo da Vinci and Michelangelo have excelled at both. But to get to business, I understand from Steele that you wish to build a kind of shack on my estate. I have been thinking the matter over and I am really terribly afraid that it is impossible. I don't mind how long you camp, but I simply cannot let you erect a building."

"Perhaps Mr Steele did not explain exactly what we want," said Christopher. "In our own interests we would not build an unsightly place; it would be a place to live and work in for the next two or three years, and I assure you we would cause no inconvenience."

"I am sure you would not," replied the Colonel. "It may seem selfish, but to tell you the truth I do a great deal of shooting. I believe the place you have chosen is a pheasant covert?"

"Yes, but it is at the extreme end of the wood. Behind us is nearly a mile of thick trees; it is on the boundary of your estate, so we would never be in the way of a drive."

"Unfortunately my neighbour and I sometimes shoot

together," replied the Colonel. "I do feel selfish, but if I give you permission to build your hut I couldn't refuse others. I keep up this estate just for the pheasant and partridge shooting, and if there were people living all over the downs there wouldn't be a bird left."

"I hope you don't think this idea of ours is just a whim," Christopher said.

"No, I certainly don't," answered the Colonel. "I believe your object is to live near the soil, not only in a way that you can work, but in a way that you can live cheaply. I think it's sound, and in many ways I would be pleased to have you here."

"If it wasn't so difficult to find a suitable spot," said Christopher, "we wouldn't worry you. In ten days we have only found two possible places. Couldn't we make an arrangement by which we would move if you found we interfered with your shooting?"

"I appreciate all you say," said Colonel Sage. "Believe me, I have thought over the matter carefully, but I can't see my way clear to let you erect a building. By all means camp as long as you please."

"Well," said Christopher, perhaps even more disappointed than I, "there's nothing to be gained by worrying you, but when I think of the extent of your property"—here Christopher smiled politely at the Colonel—"I can't help suggesting that there is just a fragment of reality in your confession of selfishness."

The Colonel returned the smile good-naturedly.

"I have a small cottage on the downs and the tenants are moving this year," he said, after a moment's thought.

" If you would like to give me your address, I will let you know when it becomes vacant. Of course, I can't promise anything."

" Thank you," I said, " but we must get fixed up before the spring. It wouldn't be worth waiting on the chance that the cottage became available."

" I suppose not," replied the Colonel. " Now tell me, how are you off for supplies in the camp? Would you like some dessert or wine? "

" I think," said I, glancing at Christopher, " we're short of wine more than dessert."

The Colonel pulled a bell-cord beside the fireplace, and in a few minutes a butler appeared.

" I want you to fetch some wine, Harris," said our host. " Would you like claret or burgundy? "

Christopher said we would like claret.

" Bring up a bottle of the best claret, Harris."

When Harris returned we thanked the Colonel for the wine and prepared to leave. He escorted us half-way down the drive, insisting on how much he would like to have given us the land, but how impossible it was for him to do so, and after shaking us warmly by the hand returned to the great house.

" Artful devil! " remarked Christopher, as soon as we were out of hearing. " He wouldn't risk his popularity for the sake of a bottle of claret."

" Popularity! " I echoed. " It would cost him a lot in spirits to keep his popularity with me! "

" Curse all the dogs-in-the-manger of this earth! " said Christopher, suddenly giving way to his anger and holding up the bottle as if he were going to dash it to pieces in the middle of the Colonel's drive.

We both fell into a dejected silence. We passed through the great gates and reached the field, we untied the pony and the dog and without a word solemnly started off back to the village.

⚡ XIII ⚡

It was almost dark when we entered the village after our unsuccessful interview with Colonel Sage. The rain was falling fast like a cold November drizzle, and as we trudged along, leading a bedraggled pony and dog, our eyes were cast earthward and our spirits were as damp as the night. At intervals we would raise a hand to tuck up our coat collars or pull down our hats over our eyes, but neither of us attempted to speak or even to relight the saturated cigarettes hanging from our lips.

Through both our minds were passing the same depressing thoughts. The downs were owned either by the War Office, by gentlemen, or by gentlemen farmers. Our enterprise was futile. Above all, did we want to go on hunting about, begging for land to build a hut? If we built it would we want to stay? To-morrow, would I be content only to move a few miles across the downs? Would I not rather travel on, to village after village, until darkness forced us to find a lane in which to pitch our tent? Did I not want to meet again Ira Lovell and travel with him and others whose fires we had sat beside, but with whom we had never travelled nor camped? Was there not something in my blood which demanded more than the soil?

Had we known the similarity of each other's thoughts we would have been less silent, but, as it was, all the way from the house of the big gates to the village we were sure of the disappointment one would feel if he knew the other's mind. A new enterprise had arisen from the remnants of the old. Nevertheless, there was something depressing in giving up a plan which had afforded us such pleasant prospects.

" Let's go to the Half Moon to-night and cheer ourselves up," said Christopher at length.

" Yes," I said, " I suppose we leave here to-morrow? "

" I suppose so, there's nothing to keep us here now."

It was only half-past five when we reached the sign of the Half Moon, and after leaving the pony in a dry stable, to which the landlord had given us access, we walked up the road with the intention of buying Sally a feed of crushed oats. Presently we came to a farm where, on entering the yard, we found a light burning in the stable. I opened the door and looked in; it was a long, narrow building of ten or more stalls, lighted by three storm lamps hanging from the beams. There was a peaceful munching noise going on when we entered, and it was only broken by a kick against the stalls or the voice of the carter who was feeding and cleaning down a team of cart-horses that had evidently just come in from the plough.

I spoke, and the man, dandy brush in hand, came forward and demanded our business.

" I want a few crushed oats," said Christopher, holding out a bag.

" A few crushed oats? " repeated the carter. " Do you want me to give them you? "

" No," I said. " We are willing enough to pay for them."

The carter put his dandy brush in a hole in the wall and,

taking one of the hurricane lamps, led us through a door into a small shed at the back of the stables.

" It wouldn't do for the governor to see you here," said the carter, picking up a miller's shovel and digging it into an immense corn bin. " I've nothing against you myself, but the boss has an abomination for travelling folk such as yourselves. Hold the bag up if you please."

When the carter had given us the oats he took us across the yard to a barn, where he cut us half a bag of sweet clover hay and advised us to slip out of the way before we were seen.

" How much are we to pay you? " I said.

" Nothing," replied the carter. " Just slip out of the way before the governor finds you here."

At this moment I heard some one crossing the yard, and the carter, opening a small door in the corner of the barn, told us to avoid the bull and walk over the fields to the village. We did as he directed and on reaching the Half Moon I went into the pony's stable and mixed up a good feed of oats and chaff in the manger. It was still only a quarter to six, but after our long walk we were both tired and hungry, and knocking at the back door of the inn we asked the landlord if he would serve us with a meal.

So much have inns ceased to afford facilities for the traveller that, had we not been well acquainted with the landlord, I doubt if we would have been favoured with more than a plate of bread and cheese when the bar opened. I hope the public-house or the inn will never cease to be a place in which the solitary traveller may find a fire and some one with whom to talk, but its real significance is lost; it is no longer the institution by which all those who set out on a journey depend, the institution which for centuries has mixed all classes together under one roof. The innkeeper has ceased to depend on the traveller, just as the traveller has ceased to depend on the inn. Indeed, I think many of the innkeepers of to-day would be better suited to superintending a provincial temperance hotel, or a café, than an English country inn. I have no complaints about the landlord of the Half Moon at ——, but in every county in England I have become accustomed to the pompous big man, or the miserable little man, who hurries into the public bar and asks the man with the accordion or the man singing to leave. Worse! I am even accustomed to seeing inoffensive men turned away for no better reason than the raggedness of their coats. An affair of this nature happened to me only a few months ago.

It was a week before Christmas, when, as Ambrose Cooper and Seth Hearne said, there should be goodwill on earth among men. We had been camping with the Coopers and the Hearnes on the heath, near Half-way House in Dorset, and on the Sunday morning to which I refer we were starting back to Wiltshire.

"Will you meet us at the *kitchimir* [public-house] agen' the Potteries on the —— Road?" said Ambrose, coming up to us when we were harnessing our horses for the journey. "Seth, me, and the boys is driving the pony to Stoke—to see if we can make a chop for Mark's colt. Your *grys* [horses] have a heavy load. If we are back there before you, we'll wait."

They jumped up behind the horse and with the trap swaying from side to side disappeared over the heath. Shortly after twelve we reached the foot of the hill, from where we could see in the distance the public-house " agen' the Potteries." We knew that our friends could not have been waiting many minutes, and it was with great surprise that we saw the trap and pony suddenly appear on top of the hill.

Christopher, who was driving ahead, hurried on his horse and met them half-way up the hill.

" Why didn't you wait? " said I, jumping out of the trap when I had caught up with them.

" The old dogsbody wouldn't serve us," said Ambrose gloomily.

" Wouldn't serve you! " I echoed.

" No," said Christopher. " I want Ambrose and Seth to turn back."

" By all means! " I said. " But tell me, did you ask the landlord why he wouldn't serve you? "

" No," replied Seth. " He just stood in the doorway and said as he wouldn't serve us. There are many like him, brother."

" But he is obliged to give a reason," I replied.

" Ho, no, he's not, he can serve who he pleases."

" He can't! " I said. " He can't refuse a customer without a definite reason. I wish you would turn back with us."

" Very well, but I tell you, brother, it'll be of no use, unless we *trash* [frighten] him, and we're sure to get took up if we do that."

Ambrose turned his trap round and we proceeded up the hill until we reached the public-house. We drew up our horses in the courtyard and walked straight into the public bar with Ambrose, Seth, and their sons.

" Seven pints of beer, please," said Christopher, throwing two half-crowns upon the counter.

" I have already refused to serve you," said the landlord sternly.

" You have not," replied Christopher. " I have never been in this place in my life."

" I don't want any argument," returned the landlord, angrily opening the counter as if he were going to throw us out.

" Nor we," I said. " Before we go any further will you give us your reason for refusing to serve us with beer? Not one of us has entered this pub since you've been landlord."

" I have refused to serve you, and that is enough. Now get out! "

" Not until you give us a reason, and if it's not a good enough reason we'll fetch a policeman."

When the man found that we stood our ground and that the *gorgios*, sitting beside the fire, did not attempt to interfere on his behalf, he became a little cooler.

" I never serve Gypsies on principle," he said. " Now do you mind leaving my premises? "

" If a landlord refused to serve a man because he was French or German, do you imagine the law would say he was justifi——? "

But before I could finish Seth Hearne stepped in front of me and angrily thrust his fist against the landlord's face.

" You white-faced *gorgio*! " he shouted. " I don't allow any man to call me slang names. Now if you don't get behind that counter and draw the beer I'll put my fist into your ugly face, so that another time you'll mind who you are talking to!"

Suddenly two men jumped up from the fire and came forward.

"If you don't want a rough house, get off yer high horse and serve them, landlord," said one. "You've been asking for what's coming to you." He abruptly pointed to a gash in his neck. "I don't suppose you know what that is? Nor this?" he continued, observing a mark on Ambrose Cooper's wrist. "In the War we had to fight together in the same trenches, now in peace time we'll drink together in the same public-house!"

The landlord retreated behind the bar counter.

"I'll serve you once on the condition you leave immediately afterwards," said he.

"You'll serve us on no conditions at all," retorted Seth. "Now that you've upset me, I care not if you fetch every policeman in bloody Dorset. I shall bide here until closing time and drink what I want!"

The landlord reluctantly drew the beer, but before we left the public-house Ambrose Cooper and Seth Hearne had each spent a pound-note. We climbed up in our traps, but before starting off on our different journeys I could not refrain from asking Seth why he had been so annoyed at being called a Gypsy.

"My dear brother," said he, "'Gypsy' is a slang name for any wandering rogue. It is a word made up by the *gorgios*. I am a Romany and, the Devil take my breath, I'll never put up with their insulting gibberish!"

" I think it is only a corruption of the word ' Egyptian,' "
I said. " Once people thought that Romanies came from
Egypt."

" Never mind, brother, I never did like it," replied Seth.

The landlord of the Half Moon, after hanging our wet
overcoats beside the fire in the public bar, led us into the
kitchen where his wife was preparing a cooked tea of fried
eggs and vegetables. The food and the cheer of the kitchen
brightened our spirits, and at a quarter-past six, when we
heard the booming voice of the big man arriving, we got
up and went into the bar. He was extremely sympathetic
and after he had apologized for leading us to think better of
the Colonel we carried our pints of beer to the fire, where,
throwing our feet upon the mantelpiece, we fell into a
profound conversation upon the strangeness of human
nature.

As the evening drew on, one by one customers arrived.
Some hurried into the bar, gulped down a pint of beer, and,
muttering something about the ' missus,' disappeared as
quickly as they came. Others ordered their beer, their
matches, their tobacco, and with a contented sigh sat down
beside the fire and thrust the poker into the hot coals. It was
a raw night, and the poker, which they used for warming
the beer, was kept in continual use by all the newcomers,
who, shaking the rain off their coats and blowing into their
cold hands, gradually flocked into the bar.

" Do you never use a copper beer-warmer? " I asked one
of the newcomers, who was submerging the red-hot iron
in the seething liquor.

" Not often," retorted the man. " The iron oxide which the poker leaves in the beer is worth all the tonic in a chemist's shop ! "

" I don't disbelieve you," I said. " When you have finished with the poker, I will try it myself."

The man replaced the poker in the fire and while it was heating I borrowed a hurricane lamp and a bucket from the landlord and went round to the stables, where I watered the pony. The night was wetter and colder than before, and when I had shut the stable door I hurried back to the bar. I took the poker out of the fire and after tapping it briskly on the irons of the grate submerged it slowly in a tankard of beer. The hot beer tasted as good as it looked and smelt; but before I go any further I feel I should give a word of warning to any who, having never before drunk beer in this way, might be tempted on a winter's night to do so in their own homes. The following December I learnt a bitter lesson.

On that stormy night when we crossed the Yorkshire Wolds in our caravan I caught a shocking cold; and the next evening, having pulled up in a lane near Driffield, I undressed and climbed straight into my bunk. For the first time since we left the Half Moon I thought again of the hot beer and the poker, and, reminding Christopher about it, I asked him to walk to the nearest village and bring back a bottle of beer and a drop of whisky. I lay in my bunk reading and smoking, and at ten o'clock I heard him returning down the lane.

Christopher climbed up the steps, and the waggon lurched forward on the springs.

" You didn't forget my beer? " said I, rather huskily (for my throat was dry) as he opened the door.

" No, it's a good drop of ale," said Christopher cheerfully. " I had three bottles of it myself. The village is a fine old place. A clergyman was sitting in the pub drinking a pint of beer when I arrived—a really sensible clergyman. I had quite a long talk with him."

" I am sorry I was not with you. I haven't often seen a clergyman in a pub."

" Nor I," went on Christopher, shutting the door behind him. " I walked up the road with an old man. He said that the *rye* who owns these fields is never about in the mornings."

" Splendid," I said. " You remembered the whisky? "

" I did," retorted Christopher good-naturedly. He thrust the poker into the fire. " You'll have your beer poker-fashion? "

" By all means," I replied, licking my lips.

Christopher discarded his overcoat and stood the bottle of beer (labelled " Nut Brown ") on the table. He then reopened the door and went outside.

" *Mandi jal* to *poove* the *gry* [I'll go and put the horse in a field]," he called out, as he descended the waggon steps.

I heard him untie the horse from the waggon wheel and open the gate into an adjoining field. In a few moments he was back. He poured the beer into a pint mug, then removing the red-hot poker from the fire plunged it in the seething ale.

" And what about the whisky? " I demanded, sitting up.

" You had better drink a drop of the beer first."

" No," I said. " Tip it in, they'll go down better together."

My brother opened a small flask containing a double of whisky and poured its contents into the steaming beer.

" *Kooshto bock* [good luck]!" said I, putting the mug to my lips.

I took a long draught, but before the hot liquor reached my stomach I choked it back so furiously that my brother immediately sprang and took refuge behind the cupboard door.

" The Devil have mercy on me ! " I ejaculated, spluttering and spitting in an effort to rid my mouth of a vile taste. " Is t-this some hor-horrible trick of yours? "

" What on earth's the matter with you? " said Christopher, looking at me with astonishment.

" Taste it ! " I choked. " Taste it, and see for yourself ! "

Christopher lifted the mug to his lips and cautiously sipped the filthy liquor.

" Good heavens ! " he said.

I lay back in my bunk, exhausted. Christopher picked up the bottle and held it to the light. A drop still remained in the bottom and, holding the neck of the vessel to his lips, he tasted it.

" There is nothing wrong with this ! " said he, handing the bottle to me. " Try it for yourself ! "

I tasted and, sure enough, there was nothing wrong with the beer.

The " Nut Brown " ale had been spoilt by heating. Few bottled beers will withstand heat, least of all " Nut Brown "; the chemicals used in bottling become, as it were, infused. I

ROMANY WOMAN

cannot tell you what chemicals are used, nor can I tell you the cause of the infusion, but I'll swear that you'll be as sick as a dog if you drink more than one mouthful of hot " Nut Brown " ale. If you feel disposed to a pint of hot beer (unless you keep a four and a half in the back kitchen) I would advise you to put an empty wine-bottle in your pocket, walk along to the nearest public-house, and ask the landlord to fill it with draught beer. Many public-houses in England have a special department for the sale of beer to be consumed off the premises. It is called the Jug and Bottle Department. A landlord, however, will never mind filling your bottles in the ordinary public bar. Indeed, I would go so far as to say that in nine cases out of ten it is advisable for a man (providing he is prepared for a glass of ale during the transaction) to ignore this specified department. An exploration of the Jug and Bottle Department might be found embarrassing by one inexperienced in its customs. It is generally a tiny little room, not more than twelve by eight feet square, the windows are glazed, and a narrow seat is built round the walls. It is really more of a cabin than a room. Inside I have invariably been confronted by a group of rather respectable women, who start nervously as if they had been caught in the middle of a shady transaction. Bottles of stout, ' home-brewed,' and gin are guiltily slipped into shopping baskets, some of the women scurry away, others sit and stare at the intruder with deep suspicion. Under this feminine scrutiny I have never stayed in the Jug and Bottle Department long enough to get through a transaction.

At the Half Moon, however, we were troubled with none

of these misfortunes. The draught beer was nicely adapted to heating, and as we sat beside the fire, drinking and talking, we began to discuss some of the many customs which, in the years gone by, must have made country life so different from what it is to-day.

" I can remember the days when we used to bide in this old pub, a-singing and dancing, from seven o'clock in the evening till nearly midnight," said an old man with an Irish voice, removing a genuine meerschaum pipe from his mouth. " Many a fine winter's night I spent here, the landlord playing his fiddle and Kirwan Fletcher his concertina."

" That reminds me," said a younger man, looking up at the landlord. " It's a main long time since I saw yer old fiddle."

" My old fiddle? " repeated the landlord. " It's a main long time ago I did see it myself! "

" You play a fiddle? " I said, looking with interest at the landlord.

" I used to play."

" Then I wish you'd fetch it to-night and play us a tune," said Christopher. " I haven't heard a fiddle for a long time."

The landlord smiled.

" No," said he, shaking his head. " I don't know where to find it, nor little more how to play it! "

" Go on! " said the old man with the pipe. " Tell the missus to fetch it down. I warrant you can play it as well as any man in the county."

" No, I tell you I haven't picked the thing up for years."

" Anyhow, I doubt if I could find the bow and the resin to save my life."

" I shall not be satisfied until I've heard it," said Christopher.

" Very well," said the landlord. " If I can find it, I'll give you one tune."

He left the bar, and after several minutes had passed he returned with a dusty old violin which he held up to the lamp and closely examined.

" I'm afraid the worms have got at 'un," said he. " Maybe it's a good thing I did bring 'un down."

At this moment the landlady came into the bar with the bow and the resin. When the instrument had been dusted and the bow prepared, the landlord came out into the room, where, provided with a chair, he sat down and tuned his fiddle. He rested the instrument on his knees and his left shoulder like some of the old Irish fiddlers.

" What shall I play you? " he asked.

" Why, play an Irish jig! " cried the old man with the pipe.

The landlord began fiddling a lively jig, which he executed so spiritedly and yet so delicately that, had it not been for the condition of the instrument, I would have thought him in as good practice as the wandering fiddlers of County Clare. There was a peculiar subtlety and ease with which he moved his bow to the quick Irish jig time.

When the landlord had finished playing he was applauded loudly and given as many drinks as he could manage. The old man with the meerschaum and the Irish voice then stood up and said that if " Mr Landlord " would play for him

he would entertain the company with an old Irish song.
" Mr Landlord " retuned his fiddle, and, having given the
bowstring another rub up, the old Irishman withdrew his
pipe from his mouth and held it before him as if to com-
mand attention.

With a final flourish of the old man's pipe and the landlord's fiddle the song ended. The big man, observing with
approval both the applause and the beer which the per-
formers were given, drew himself up and removing his
hat said :

" Now if the landlord can accompany me, I'll sing you
a good old poaching song."

" What's it called, Scout? " said the landlord.

" I don't know what it's called," replied Scout. " But
it's a good old song and it starts :

> " It's my delight on a shining night
> In the season of the year. . . ."

" *The Lincolnshire Poachers!* If you sing it well, by God,
I'll give you a quart of beer ! " said the Irishman, who, like
the rest of the company, was feeling very generous.

The old man certainly did sing it well, he sang it with
feeling, and no one begrudged the beer which they stood
him.

It was a merry, enjoyable evening that we spent at the
Half Moon, and at ten o'clock, when the company broke
up, the landlord said :

" It's a long time since we had a night like this ! "

" You speak the truth ! " said the Irishman. " In these
days we're forgetting how to enjoy ourselves."

Outside the old barn we shook hands with Scout and wished him good-bye. It was still raining when we started back to the camp, but after our evening at the Half Moon we felt in much better spirits. I lit a cigarette, which, after so much beer, tasted good in the night air.

" Where shall we go to-morrow? " I asked, suddenly making an effort to discover my brother's thoughts.

" Do you want to look for another place here? "

" Not particularly. I should rather like to make a long move."

" In another month the spring will be here," said Christopher. " With a trap and a bigger tent I believe we could work travelling about the country."

I was elated to discover that our thoughts were similar.

" Then," I said, " unless we break-in the pony, we must make a chop for another turn-out."

On approaching our camp we heard the faint bleat of a sheep. Evidently the shepherd had visited the camp during the afternoon, for the ewe, which was stronger and now able to move its head and legs a little, was lying on its other side. The rain had not leaked or blown into the tent, and, after tethering the pony, we wriggled into our beds and fell asleep.

⚮ XIV ⚮

How quickly the weather changes!" I said, as we sat over the fire waiting for the kettle to boil early the next morning.

The time was little more than seven o'clock, but beyond the shadow of the pine-trees the sun was quite warm and in the air was a feeling of spring. Despite the pleasant prospects which our sudden change of plans afforded us, we could not suppress a feeling of regret when we pulled down the tent and prepared to leave the hill of the pine-trees. The sheep was now well on the path to recovery and we left her on a bed of hay under a dog-rose bush.

It was a warm sunny morning with scarcely a cloud in the sky when we made our way along the old Roman road past the ruined hovel, where nearly a week ago we had camped. Out on the hard road we made better pace and by one o'clock we had covered the six miles which divided the village from Warminster. As we approached the town, recalling our last visit, I suggested carrying Nell through Warminster.

"No," said Christopher. "If you carry her she'll be just as noticeable."

"Then let us miss out Warminster," I suggested.

My brother would listen to none of my proposals and at length we marched boldly into the town, one leading the pony, the other the dog. At a little shop we halted and laid in a day's provisions, then, despite the stopping and staring of the townspeople, we entered the main street with great *aplomb*. I was thinking how a small herd of Kashmir goats would add to our splendour when I heard a muttered oath from Christopher and, looking up, I saw that the baggage had slid to one side and was ready, without a moment's warning, to scatter itself in the middle of the roadway. Christopher hissed his directions and, pushing, shouldering, tugging, I readjusted the load. In a low voice I told him that all was safe, but scarcely had I spoken, scarcely had we gone another half-dozen yards, when the pony stood still and shook herself fiercely.

Christopher jabbed the pony with his fists, and looked cautiously to see if the onlookers were observing his anger.

I struggled breathlessly to prevent the bundle, which had slid half-way over her back, from reaching the ground and causing the customary entanglement. Christopher left the animal's head and rushed to help me. By our united efforts we pushed the load back into place, but this time at the critical moment a steam lorry roared past, and Sally, who had an abomination for all fiery vehicles, reared and darted forward. As I ran to stop her I noticed that a crowd of people had collected on the pavement. I grabbed the animal by the bridle, but before I could bring her to a standstill I heard a shout from Christopher, followed immediately by a peal of laughter from the people on the pavement. All our belongings had swung to the ground with a crash and were now grovelling in the dust of the High Street. The milk, which we had only just purchased, ran across the road in streams and, in spite of our redoubled efforts, the wretched pony struggled and kicked her way up the road, dragging with her the ropes, the blankets, and the pots and pans.

When we had disentangled everything from the pony's legs I tied her to a lamp-post, while Christopher, livid, dragged our belongings clear of the passing traffic. No one on the pavement appeared to think of offering us help, and after what seemed hours we repacked the last utensil and secured the ropes. At the first public-house we stopped and each drank a pint of beer. We then hurried out of the town as quickly as we could.

The sun set and still we kept travelling. A low white mist rose slowly from the river and the meadows on either side of the road. The redness on the horizon disappeared, the traffic lit up; and still the clatter of the pony's shoes and the steady tramping of our feet resounded on the hard road, and echoed among the trees when our path led us through a wood or copse. The stars appeared one by one until the heavens were brilliant. The mist lifted and hung over the meadows, then, as the frost came, the air became dry and keen so that our breath appeared like clouds of steam.

" Let's find a lane and stop for the night," I said, beginning to feel hungry and tired.

We had been travelling on a by-road which, since Warminster, had taken us through the lowlands of Wiltshire to the borders of Somerset. The country was flat, open, unpopulated, and before long we came to a wide green lane, enclosed on either side by trees and thick hedges. After examining the lane we led the pony to a dry sheltered corner, out of sight of the road. Then having unpacked we pitched the tent close against the hedge, after which Christopher collected dry wood and lit a fire, while I went in search of a pond or a running stream. I hunted about the fields for some time, but I could only find an old drinking-trough, the water in which was stagnant and smelt vilely when I stirred it. I examined the ball-cock of the trough and when I found that it worked I returned to the camp for a cup and a bowl, with which I bailed out the stagnant water until I could hold the cup under the valve and catch the fresh water.

No one disturbed us during the evening and, after we had supped, smoked, and drunk half the Colonel's bottle of wine, we crawled into the tent. Directly our heads touched the ground we fell asleep until the morning.

At daybreak I awoke and found the lane and the fields white as if there had been a fall of snow during the night. I shifted the pony to a fresh place and, strolling down the lane, which in the grip of the frost was as hard as stone, began collecting wood for breakfast. There was little to be found without pulling the hedges about, but presently I managed to hook a dead branch out of an ash-tree and another couple of hundred yards up the lane I found an elm-tree thickly covered with dead ivy wood, most of which I stripped off and carried back to the camp. There's nothing that burns and smells better than dry ivy wood. As soon as I had lit the fire I called my brother, who dressed and, picking up the kettle, sleepily trudged off in the direction of the water-trough.

The sun rose and appeared through the trees and hedges across the low meadowland. Slowly it climbed above the branches of the elm-trees and inch by inch the shadows across the fields shortened.

After camping at night in a strange part of the country it is pleasant to awake the next morning and discover your surroundings, which are often quite different from your expectations. On a dark night it is sometimes impossible to estimate even roughly the type of country, and although the morning usually brings a pleasant surprise, on several occasions I have received something of a shock.

Several months later we were travelling in Berkshire; we could not find a place to stop with our waggon and we continued to wander along the roads until the early hours of the morning. At two o'clock, half asleep, we passed through the village of P—— on the borders of Buckinghamshire; it was so dark we could not see beyond the light of the candle lamps and, finding what appeared to be a common or a wide grass verge, we drew the waggon off the road. As we passed over a steep dip, which in the darkness had looked only slight, the furniture and most of the crockery was upset inside the waggon. We straightened things out, attended to the horse, and we went to bed. I looked out of the window early in the morning and saw a great mansion house within a stone's throw of the waggon. We had camped in the park in front of P—— Manor! I awakened my brother and we crept half dressed out of the waggon with the intention of harnessing the horse and quietly moving away before we were seen. The horse had gone! The broken end of a halter rope hung from the waggon wheel, and the hay which we had put out before going to bed was scarcely touched. The dip in the bank, over which we had passed in the night, was like an immense trench. There was no flat place by which we could safely return to the road, and when the horse was found we had to make a grand tour of the grounds before we could escape.

I hardly know whether we had a greater shock when we awoke on a Cornish moor, and found that we had camped three or four yards from the open shaft of an old tin mine. The night before the wheels of the waggon had passed within three inches of the edge.

Then there was the time when we camped in a paddock behind a public-house in Devonshire. At night, when we staggered back to the camp, we had one big horse, but in the morning when we awoke there were two small ponies. I shall never forget what I went through as I lay under the cart, staring at two moorland ponies who had entered the paddock by the gate which we had left open and by which our own horse had escaped.

There was, however, an occasion on which a shock and a pleasant surprise were combined in one awakening. We were travelling in Yorkshire, we had no maps, and one evening having been turned out of a lane by an old woman who owns a tidy bit of East Riding, we wandered into the night and after travelling at least twelve miles we pulled up in a field of corn stubble which lay unfenced against the road. In the morning, long before it was light, we were mystified by a strange rumbling noise, which grew louder and louder as day approached. At last I sat up and looked out of the back window of the waggon; there was a peculiar freshness in the air, but it was still not light enough to see more than the corn stubble around us. I watched, the dawn broke, and a seagull flew past the waggon. In my half-asleep, mystified mind I realized the roaring to be the noise of sea breakers and the rumbling the thunder of subsiding cliff.

I called Christopher and together we watched the sun rise over the North Sea. The corn stubble ran to the edge of the red earth cliffs, which at nearly every tide were eroded more and more. We had no idea that we were even near the coast, and we had camped within forty yards of the cliff's edge.

After we had breakfasted and the fire died down we fetched the pony and began packing. At nine o'clock we led the pony back to the road, where at a good all-round pace we set off in the direction of Bruton and Wincanton, in Somerset. The country was green and, although culti-vated, wild and lovely. The only buildings were farms, set back at some distance from the road, and mostly shel-tered by lofty elm-trees. We had left the lowlands of Wilt-shire behind us, and the narrow lane on which we travelled was for ever ascending or descending.

Presently we came to a little village and finding that the public-house was open we went inside and ordered a plate of bread and cheese and two small beers. It was an old stone-roofed inn, and both the furniture and the old woman who served us appeared to be as ancient as the building itself; the table at which we ate was a slab of oak on three legs; the benches were made of equally stout material;

the floor was laid with uneven blue stones; and the brilliantly polished copper beer-warmers and pots which hung on either side of the great fireplace gave the place an air of medieval simplicity and grandeur. Indeed, except for the worn, uneven, stone floor, the place must have looked exactly the same as it did in the days of James I.

I finished my beer and was just thinking of ordering my glass to be refilled when I heard the pony whinny and the sound of a horse coming down the street in the direction of the inn at a hammering trot. We went to the window and presently we saw a piebald pony drawing a four-wheel dog-cart, in which were seated two women, a girl, and several children, who all looked and pointed with great interest at Sally and the load on her back. The younger of the two women was driving, the old woman who sat beside her was smoking a short clay pipe, and in the back of the trap a girl was doing her best to prevent three dark little children from falling out onto the road.

The horse stopped opposite the inn, the women took out their hawking baskets and, leaving the girl with the trap, disappeared down a lane with the children.

Five or six minutes must have elapsed and then, hearing more horses, we returned to the window and saw a man and a boy leading two black horses. The man wore a black hat, a black silk handkerchief round his neck, and a suit cut and stitched in the old Gypsy pattern. The boy, who was about twelve years old, wore a cap on one side of his head, a coloured handkerchief round his neck, a coat of the same pattern as the man, and long corduroy trousers. He ran along with a freeness of movement that I could not avoid noticing and, looking more closely, I saw that he had neither shoes nor stockings on his brown feet. It is only with the greatest difficulty that Gypsy parents induce their children to put on boots or shoes, and then at the slightest provocation off they come and the dark bare feet tear over the fields, leaving the cumbersome shackles forgotten in the hedge.

They went up to the girl who was looking after the trap and, after speaking with her for a moment, led the horses over to the inn. They tied up beside our pony and walked into the bar, where the man, after wishing us good morning, ordered a pint of ale and a glass of lemonade for the boy.

" That's a nice little pony you have outside," said the man, when the landlady had gone to draw the beer.

" Yes, she's a good little animal. Are you stopping near by? " I said.

" In an old lane about fifteen minutes' drive from here. Tell me, how far have you come to-day? " said the Gypsy.

" About ten miles."

" Not like that, brother? " exclaimed the Gypsy, pointing in the direction of our pony.

" Yes, like that," said I.

" But surely, brother, in this country it is a strange way to travel? "

" No doubt it's a strange way to travel in this part of the world," answered Christopher smiling, " but it is common enough in many parts."

" Then I make no doubts you come from those parts? "

" No, we were born and bred in the next county. But as a matter of fact we intend to get a better turn-out," I said.

"I am not surprised," replied the Gypsy, paying the landlady and taking a draught of his beer. "Here there are good roads 'most everywhere, and, for my part, I wouldn't travel in that fashion for all the gold sovereigns in the world."

"I daresay you have waggons?"

"Yes, brother, we have three waggons. My father and mother have one for themselves, my *chavies* have one just to lie in, but my own is of little good to me, for my woman will not lie in a waggon; indeed, she will have nothing to do with a waggon and is as miserable as a cow until I help her put up a *lue*."

"What do you call a *lue*?"

"Have you never heard of a *lue*?"

"No," I said. "I cannot remember having heard the word."

"Well, it is just a word for a high tent, with a hole in the top for the smoke of the fire to draw out."

"But tell me," said Christopher, "why won't your wife sleep in a waggon?"

"I hardly know for why, brother," answered the Gypsy. "She comes from the Hearne family—they are an old-fashioned lot and many of them have never taken to waggons. One night, when first she and me come together, I made her lie up in the waggon. I shall never forget it, we hadn't been in bed a couple of hours when an unlucky storm blew up and shook the waggon from side to side, like as if it were a boat on the high seas. All night long she cried and fought and struggled, and I can tell you, brother, I never again tried to sleep wi' her in a waggon."

"I suppose she is afraid of it blowing over?"

"It is not altogether that, young man. If you can understand me, my little woman and all her people who 'ave lived afore 'er were born and bred in tents; they've always a-led on the ground, and nothing will ever break 'em of it."

"Have you been travelling much this winter?" I said, rolling a cigarette and handing the tobacco and papers to the man.

"We have, young man, I've had no rest from travelling since last hop-picking." He looked at the tobacco, then smelt it. "I fancy this is too light for me—do you mind if I have one of your papers and use my own shag?" He pulled a small tin of Black Beauty out of his waistcoat pocket and rolled himself a cigarette. "I should have thought a waggon would have just suited two young fellows like yourselves."

"It would be very heavy for travelling," I said.

"No, it wouldn't," replied the Gypsy. "A good horse will get a waggon anywhere."

"Tell me, do you travel with waggons all the year round?"

"No, brother, we only uses waggons in the wintertime. We generally gets rid of the waggons just before Devizes Fair. Traps and two or three good rod tents is all we takes in the summer. I have a tidy waggon I'll sell you cheap. It is sadly in need of a coat of paint, but it is a beautiful waggon and if you spent a little time and money on it you'd have one of the finest waggons in this part of the country."

"Is it big?"

" Yes, it's a big waggon, but a good horse would draw it anywhere. Will you come up to my place and take a look at it? "

" I don't think we'll trouble you," said Christopher. " For I doubt if we could raise the money to buy a waggon."

" Then perhaps we could make a chop for the pony? " said the man. " But if we don't trade, it'll be of no account, for I shall be glad of your company."

" Well, we'd like to look at the waggon," said Christopher. " And, as you say, if we don't trade there'll be no harm done. I see you've finished your beer. Will you have a drink with us? "

" Thank you," said the man. " It is not often I drink in the day-time, but to-day I have bought two good horses, and when I saw your pony tied up outside I thought I'd have a look in and see who was here."

" I'm glad you did," said I; then, turning to the boy, I asked him what he would drink.

" If you please, a glass of bitter shandy," said the boy. Then after a moment's hesitation he touched me on the back. " Don't tell the old woman who it's for," he said.

I asked him why.

" Because she won't serve you," he whispered.

Before long I heard the women returning to the trap, and the Gypsy, after walking to the window and looking out, turned to the boy and said:

" Markie! Go and fetch in yer mother and yer granny. Tell 'em I want 'em."

" It's not a bit of good for me to go," said Markie, retreating to the farthest corner of the bar. "You know as they'll not come for me."

"They are as likely to come for you as me," said the man, rather worriedly. "It's a pity we didn't think of putting the horses in the back yard, where they wouldn't have set eyes on 'em."

I went to the window. The women were standing beside the trap facing the inn, as if watching for the exits of the guilty Markie and his father, who both exchanged harassed looks across the bar.

The two women stood with their eyes glued to the door of the White Horse. They were good-looking women, the older in her age, and the younger in her youth. Resolutely Markie's grandmother smoked. At first the pipe scarcely seemed alight, but the longer she waited the more fiery it became. Clouds of blue smoke partly enveloped the old woman's features and bonnet, and I quickly began to feel a little concern as to how long the tobacco in that short, stumpy clay pipe would last. I was anxious to visit the camp of Markie's father, but I knew from experience that it was important to start on good terms with the women if we wished to be welcome guests. I was about to make a suggestion when the man turned to us.

"Will one of you come out wi' me and bring in the womenfolk?" he said. "I make no doubt they'll take a bit more notice of you."

"Yes, I'll ask them to drink a glass of stout with us," said Christopher, putting down his mug.

They started to the door, but in an instant I saw that it was too late. The smoke was no longer coming from

178

Granny's pipe. She drew several times, but it was out, and taking it from her lips she pushed it in her pocket and walked across the road to the inn. At the doorway she met Christopher and the Gypsy; I looked at Mark, and grinning broadly he said:

"Now there'll be summat a-going! I thinks you and me is better out of it."

A sudden burst of raised voices echoed down the passage, and Mark covering his face with his hands groaned.

"*Dick kie!* [Look there!]" he exclaimed. "Now they're at it!"

I went into the passage and found Granny demanding to know why her son could not bide away from a public-house, and why he insisted on frittering away the little money that his wife and his old mother had struggled to earn. The younger woman demanded to know the same and, indeed, so loudly did they clamour for this information that it was some time before the man could make himself heard. At intervals Christopher repeated his invitation to the women, but each time it was unheard and, as the man began also to lose his temper, he became less importunate until finally he stood to one side and was silent. I thought of a solution and returning to the bar I ordered two pints of draught stout. I carried them out to the women, but until the man, who was now railing at his wife and mother for their interference, angrily observed how they were ignoring our friendly entreaties. we might have been the stones of the passage wall.

"Let the young men drink their own bloody stout!" cried Granny savagely. "It's wickedness to bide here and rob the young men of their money. They must be as poor as church mice to go about the country like this ! "

The stout was sternly refused, and the Gypsy, having observed his womenfolk's ignorance of good company, told them plainly to go to the devil. They had upset him, he said, and now their foolish jabber would not prevent him from sitting down beside the fire and enjoying an hour's talk with the young strangers.

The younger woman made a last effort to discover the whereabouts of her son and then returned to the trap with Granny, where they put up their hawking baskets and drove out of the village. We returned to the bar with the Gypsy and the three of us sat down beside the fire.

" Women are a trial, brother," said the man, sighing deeply. " Whatever makes 'em like it? "

" Do they always get upset when you go into a public-house? " I asked.

" No, brother, they don't always get upset when I goes into a public-house, for sometimes they'll drink too much themselves. But to-day they know I've a deal o' money on me, and they are afraid that I shall get drunk and throw it away. You see, my little woman takes care of the *vongar* [money]; this morning she gave me what I required for trading purposes—it was thirty-five sovereigns, brother— and now from the horses I've a-bought and sold she can *dick* [see] that I have from fifteen to twenty pounds left. If, as is usually the case, brother, I had nothing but a shilling in my pockets she would not care a brass farthing whether I went in or stayed out of a public-house."

" No doubt you have often been *mawto* [drunk] when

you have had money in your pockets," suggested Christopher.

" Yes, brother, I have often gone home very drunk; and at a fair I was once robbed of ten pounds while I lay helpless on the ground. The truth is, brother, for generations the women have looked after the money; a travelling man is handy enough on a deal, but when it comes to spending, brother, he's got no sense. It is a strange state of affairs, but a man has come to look to his woman over money matters. But I see I've been drinking the stout you bought for my womenfolk; now will you kindly finish your beer and call the landlady? "

I drained my mug and the Gypsy man asked to be served with half a gallon of beer in a jug.

While the three of us sat beside the fire drinking and talking about waggons, horses, and the affairs of wandering folk, young Mark amused himself at the dart board. He chattered to himself as he threw the darts and, having made three treble sixties in rotation, he challenged me to a game.

" No, Mark," I said, " but I'll play you a game of shove-ha'penny."

" That's it, Markie," said the boy's father. " Play the young man a game of shove-ha'penny, and when you've finished I'll play the winner on the dart-board."

The shove-ha'penny board was set on the table and when it had been polished with a bag of french chalk provided by the landlady the boy filled up the first bed with three well-directed brass ha'pennys. By the skin of my teeth I succeeded in winning the game and qualifying for the dart contest with Mark's father. Christopher then challenged

the boy to a second game of shove-ha'penny and we ended
with the winners of the two games tying on the dart-
board. We spent a pleasant couple of hours in this way
and having won, lost, and drunk as much beer as was good
for us, we bade the old woman good morning and went
out to the horses, which we untied and led out of the village in the direction of the Gypsies' camp. As we made
our way along the narrow lane, talking to Mr Ayres above
the clatter of the horses' feet and the untuneful singing of
Mark, I began to wonder what kind of a reception we
would receive from the womenfolk of the camp.

"If they are insolent to you, my brothers," said Mr
Ayres, who had evidently been occupied with the same
thoughts, "take not a bit of notice, for they'll soon find
their better temper."

But in spite of his optimism Elias Ayres was undoubtedly
worried.

"Take no offence, for they'll not mean what they say,"
he went on thoughtfully. "I like my fellow-travellers to
be welcome to my fire and my tent, but, brother, you
cannot expect them to feel welcome with two women
brooding over the fire like angry witches."

Mark, on the other hand, displayed quite a different
attitude. He lived clearly for the moment and with a com-
plete disregard of trouble until he met it face to face. He
was for ever poking about in the hedge, climbing the trees
on either side of the lane, or pointing out to us a rabbit,
a hare, or some strange bird in the near-by fields. His
interest in life was intense; every clump of grass in the
hedge, every bush or tree, or barn, or stream filled him

with a lively curiosity, which seemed to make no distance too far to run, no height too high to climb, and no ditch too wide to jump. Like a wild animal he did not appear to be conscious of physical exertion.

At length we came to a narrow grass lane where we left the road and presently came in sight of the encampment. The lane was wet and muddy, but the camp had been made on a dry raised piece of ground a mile or more from the road. Two big waggons were standing against the hedge, and between them and a small barrel-top waggon was the *lue*, from a hole in the top of which there poured clouds of blue smoke. Five or six horses, some tethered and some loose, were grazing around the camp; the waggonette which the women had been driving in the village was standing beside a light two-wheel trap, outside the great tent. Except for the smoke and the horses, who looked up and whinnied at our approach, the place seemed deserted. We fastened the pony to a wheel of the barrel-top waggon and then waited for Elias Ayres to feed the grey colts, which he had tied up to the hedge.

The great tent still remained silent and the smoke poured from the hole in the top like the clouds of dust smoke from a volcano. At length I heard the murmur of children's voices; it was only a faint, brief murmur, and it seemed to us an unnatural silence that followed.

❧ XV ❧

Eｌｉａｓ ａｙｒｅｓ ｌｅｄ ｕｓ ｄｏｗｎ ｔｈｅ ｈｅｄｇｅ ｔｏ ｔｈｅ ｂａｃｋ ｏｆ the tent, where he banged the canvas with his hand and shouted:

"Open up there, will you!"

A small hand emerged and pulled back a piece of sacking, making a gap just large enough for us to enter. We followed Elias into the tent, where we found the women sitting brooding over a great, smoke-blackened stew-pot, hanging on an iron above the fire. The auburn-haired girl who had minded the horse looked up and smiled, but her grandmother and her mother kept their eyes on the black pot, from which came an appetizing smell of Irish stew.

The interior of the tent was big and roomy, and when the gap had been covered by the sackcloth the smoke went straight up in a column. The canvas had become blackened by the smoke, and the place was illuminated more by the fire than by the little daylight that came in through the smoke-hole in the middle of the roof. This centre dome or roof was built in a circle, about eleven feet in diameter, and was supported on a framework of young ash-poles, the thick ends of which were driven into the ground and the thin ends drawn together on top. In the centre, directly below the smoke-hole, was the fire. The dome, standing at least twelve feet high, acted as a chimney, and when the draught was good the smoke was carried straight out of the tent. The atmosphere was surprisingly clear.

On either side of the dome, parallel with the hedge, were two rod tents that could be curtained off from the main living-quarters. These were the sleeping-booths, and on one of the beds a little girl of about three years slept peacefully, her small brown arms spread out on either side. The rest of the children sat beside the fire, playing with a white cat and four kittens; they were exceptionally quiet for Gypsy children, but before I had been in the tent long I noticed the twinkle in their dark eyes.

Beneath the great black pot the fire, fuelled with dry ash-wood, burnt cheerfully and steadily. Despite the cold outside it was almost too warm inside the tent, and the light from the blazing wood gave the place an atmosphere of winter cosiness. It was a strange interior scene—I think the strangest an Englishman could find in his own country.

Elias raked out two stools and a log of wood, which he placed beside the fire, before inviting us to sit down and warm ourselves. He was clearly annoyed at the inhospitable attitude of his women folk, and stirring the fire he demanded roughly whether or no the dinner was ready.

No one answered, so he took off the lid of the pot and peered inside.

" The *hobben* [victuals] is ready, gal !" he said, addressing the girl of the auburn hair and the green eyes. " Get up and fetch the *covels* [things], you lazy little mare ! "

The girl rose and dragged a hamper across the tent to her mother, who, rousing herself, opened it and took out a loaf of bread and a dozen or more dinner-plates and spoons. The great pot was swung off the fire, and the woman, having ladled the stew into the plates and cut up the loaf of bread, silently handed us our dinner. It was a strained meal, the women persisting in their silence, Elias going out of his way to anger his wife, and I was glad when I heard a pony and trap stop in the lane and a cheerful old man—whom we took to be Grandfather—blustered into the tent.

He shook us warmly by the hand and while he ate his dinner entertained us with an amusing account of a visit which he had just paid to a neighbouring squire.

Presently Elias rose and offered to show us the waggon which he had spoken of in the public-house.

" By rights you should see a waggon in the dark before you think of making a bid," said Elias, holding up the sacking while Christopher and I crawled out of the *lue*.

" Why is that? " I asked.

" Well, brother, if you light a candle in a waggon all the chinks and cracks will show up at night," he said as he led us to one of the big caravans against the hedge.

" This is the one," he went on. " It is a Reading waggon, and if it was painted and properly lined out, brother, I warrant it would be one of the prettiest *verdos* [caravans] in this part of the country."

The paintwork was rough and dirty, but I could see that there was exquisite workmanship beneath it. The design of the waggon was exceedingly graceful—the sides sloping outwards at a gentle angle, the roof curving, the back wheels, which were on the outside of the body, standing five feet high, and the structural parts, the axle casings, the porch over the door, and the edges of the roof all delicately carved.

" You see, the waggon is made throughout with penny-farthing boards," said Elias, taking a penny and a farthing from his pocket and measuring the narrow boards. " They'll never make another waggon like that, brother."

" Very true," agreed Christopher, " but it would cost a lot of money to repair the waggon. This wheel, for instance, would not last long on the roads; this longitudinal is rotten and half the leaves of the back springs are broken."

Elias produced a jack knife and dug it into the hub of the wheel which Christopher had mentioned.

" There's a good stretch of life in that wheel, brother." He withdrew the knife, and tried several members of the turn-table. " You see, brother, that's the part of the waggon that matters," he went on, observing that the knife would hardly mark the wood. " You can easily get a new wheel, but it would cost you as much as the waggon is worth to have a turn-table like that made."

Christopher borrowed the knife from Elias and went round the waggon testing the woodwork; the only badly rotted parts were those that could be inexpensively replaced, and having returned the knife we asked to look inside. Elias adjusted the steps and we followed him into the waggon. Christopher, who is over six feet tall, was able to stand upright, there were two side windows and one back (each of which had outside shutters); on the left side near the door was a neat miniature cooking-range, which had an oven and a brass rail to prevent the pots from falling when the waggon was moving.

In keeping with the Romany fashion the inside of the caravan was adorned with gold, silver, and china trinkets; indeed, anything that possessed a pleasing ornamental value was given a place in one of the little glass cupboards, or on the mantelpiece.

" Two of the children have been sleeping in the waggon," said Elias, " but, as you see, it's all clean and tidy, and if we makes a deal I'll not doubt the women will let you keep some of these little *covels*."

I looked at my brother.

" What do you think about the waggon? " I said.

" It's not a bad waggon," Christopher admitted cautiously, " but it needs repairing. I tell you what, Pat, we'll give Elias a chop for the pony."

" Very well," said I. " Will you make a chop, Elias? "

" No, brother, you could not expect me to make a level chop," Elias said. " You'd be having a great bargain if you gave me a couple of sovereigns."

" No, we couldn't give you that," said Christopher. " It must be a level chop or nothing."

" Then it must be nothing," replied Elias. " You cannot reckon your pony to be worth more than seven pounds, and I cannot reckon my waggon to be worth less than nine or ten pounds."

We went down the steps and silently repeated the examination of the waggon; we shook the wheels; shifted the waggon backwards and forwards; turned the lock; then stood back and surveyed the general effect.

"Let's have a word together," said Christopher after a few minutes' thought, and we walked along the lane, sitting down on the trunk of a fallen tree and lighting a cigarette.

"It's a good waggon," he said, "but it would be of precious little value to us without a full-sized cart-horse in the shafts."

"If it were done up properly it would fetch thirty or forty pounds."

"Still, it would be better to travel as we are than sell the pony and have to stay in one place."

"Look here," I said. "If we had bought a piece of land it would have cost us a good bit of money. Between us we can just as easily manage to buy a good horse."

"I doubt it. What do you think we'd have to pay for a good horse?"

"Anything from twenty-five to forty pounds."

"Then we would have nothing left at all," he said.

I smoked and thought for some time. It seemed that with a good waggon and a horse there would be little need for money. I said so to Christopher. He agreed, and we decided to make the deal if Elias Ayres would split the difference of two pounds. When we returned to the camp we offered him the pony and one pound in exchange for the waggon. At first he insisted on his original terms, but after half an hour's haggling he agreed to split the remaining difference, ten shillings of which we could pay at our own convenience.

We unloaded our pony, and Britannia, the girl with the auburn hair, came out of the tent and began clearing the stuff from the waggon. It was an amusing and an exciting afternoon. We helped to transfer the Ayres' belongings to the tent, the girl swept out the waggon and scrubbed the floor; the children blacked the stove and polished the brass, Elias oiled the turn-table and the wheels while Christopher and I, when we were not busy helping with the work, admired, discussed, and arranged our new home.

It was growing dark when the work was finished and all our belongings carried up the steps of the waggon.

Among travelling folk, when a caravan is exchanged or sold, it is a custom not to remove the curtains. We had lighted a pair of candles in the swivel-fittings over the mantelpiece and while we were busy arranging our belongings Priscilla, the younger sister of Britannia, ran up into the waggon and said that her mother wished to have the curtains. I helped the little girl to get them down, but I was alarmed at so startling a breach of custom, and wondered how far these women would be led by their ill-temper. Presently, however, Priscilla returned and from the bottom of the waggon steps shouted that her mother wanted us to go in for tea. Christopher blew out the candles and the little girl took us into the *lue*. Even from the outside I detected a less strained atmosphere. The children were making a reasonable amount of noise, the men were talking more, and even the smoke, glowing to a dull red by the fire beneath, seemed to pour from the top of the great tent with less restraint.

Inside we found a cheerful fire and a pleasant smell of freshly made tea. Granny, who had removed her bonnet, was sitting on the ground before the fire smoking her clay pipe; she did not speak when we came in, but she looked much less ferocious. The younger woman was busy giving the children their food, but after Elias had provided us with seats she handed us our tea and explained that she had sent Priscilla to remove the curtains because she intended replacing them with a special set of chintz waggon curtains, which she had washed and ironed during the afternoon. Granny then smiled at us benevolently and asked if we were pleased with the waggon. I told her that it was the first waggon which we had possessed ourselves and that we were very pleased with it indeed.

" Then I hopes you has good luck wi' it," said the old woman. " I have one or two little things I will give you after tea, for I'm thinking you'll not have much your-selves."

I thanked Granny, and when we had eaten our tea she took us round to her barrel-top waggon, where she lit an oil lamp and showed us her treasures. It was a well-kept waggon; the metal fittings and the stove were highly polished; the bedding and the curtains were spotlessly clean; and each of the little ornaments which decorated the interior had more than a purely ornamental value. There were numerous pieces of old English plate above the mantelshelf and in the glass cupboard by the door were several good china figures and silver and ivory statuettes of horses.

About the old woman and the waggon there lingered something of the prosperity which existed among the English Romanies of the last century. In Scotland there are still the remnants of that old splendour, but in the South of England we no longer see the magnificent waggon drawn by a team of fine piebald horses. That was a prosperity only remembered by the Romanies of Granny's generation; it was short-lived, but it sufficed to mislead many into associating prosperity with all true Gypsies. Granny often lamented the loss of the splendour of her days, but she never lamented a corresponding decline in her people. She had known the Hearnes, who had scorned the luxuries of that brief golden age, and she knew that her daughter-in-law still lived in the same type of tent that is used by the tribes who now roam the plains and deserts of Persia. 'Hedge-crawlers,' I have heard the prosperous Gypsy of Carlisle call his tent-dwelling brother. But I have also heard these hedge-crawlers, with equal contempt, refer to their prosperous brethren as ' showmen.'

Without a doubt, tents and ponies are the true possessions of a Gypsy. The more he strays from them, the quicker he loses the characteristics and customs of his race. The Gypsy musician of Budapest dislikes being classed with the wandering Gypsy of Rumania; he has become a snob, a victim of class distinction, a fatal error of which the true Gypsy is ignorant. They are an exceptionally race-proud people with strong racial prejudices, but these prejudices crystallize against all *gorgios*, who in nearly every country in the world have inflamed the Gypsy's hatred as much from fear as from contempt and persecution. In England it is strange how modern conditions, roads, cheap manufacture, and sixpenny bazaars have robbed the Gypsy of his prosperity and obliged him to return to the same raggle-taggle tent that he erected nearly four hundred years ago, when he first set foot in this country.

Elias, through the influence of the times, and his wife, had almost forgotten the splendour of the age in which his mother had lived. He liked his waggon, but he was not proud of it, and as for his children, they had not the slightest knowledge of the worldly pride that had temporarily created a love of possession and grandeur.

Granny showed us round the waggon and explained how she had come by her pieces of jewellery, her little figures and her old china. When she had finished I asked her the history of an immense gold ring which she was wearing.

"That was given me by my dear old grandmother, Naomi Cooper," she said, holding the ring up to the lamp. "Three ounces of solid gold! She wore it to rap upon the doors of the *gorgios'* houses."

Presently the old woman opened a cupboard and showed us an old framed print of Samuel Johnson.

"I'm no scholar meself," said she, "but he looke a sensible, good-natured old man and if you can tell me who he is, I thought I'd let you hang him up in your waggon."

After I had given Granny an account of Johnson and his works, she presented us with two brass candlesticks and several cups and saucers, which she said would help to make the waggon more comfortable. We thanked her warmly, returned to the van, and when we had lit a fire in the range I hung the Doctor over the mantelpiece and lit a pair of candles in the brasses. Britannia and her mother arrived soon afterwards and we helped them put up the curtains.

The greater part of the evening was spent in arranging the waggon, but at nine o'clock we went down to the great tent and sat beside the fire for an hour. Elias offered to drive us in the morning to a friend who would probably have a horse suitable for drawing our waggon. It would be a drive of ten or twelve miles, so we arranged to be up early and away soon after seven o'clock. We sat in the tent smoking and talking until the fire had died down and the ashes had been stirred until the last spark of warmth had gone. We wished the women and the children good night and went out to assist Elias in making the horses safe. Four ponies were hobbled with old stockings, which were tied across their forelegs. Sally and a two-year-old colt were tethered on plug chains, but the two grey cart colts, which Elias had bought in the morning, would neither be hobbled nor tethered, and since the night was cold and frosty there was nothing for it but to turn them loose in one of the adjoining fields.

Pooving the grys [putting the horses in a field at night], as it is known among Romanies, is a tricky business; it is a cunning Gypsy practice, but it is also something of an art. The careless Gypsy who at night turns his horses loose in the nearest field, and fetches them out early the next morning, is asking for trouble. Sooner or later he will wake up either to find that his horses' legs are broken, or that his animals are securely locked up in the stables of a near-by farm, the owner of which has prepared an alarming bill for the unauthorized night's grazing.

When we had finished hobbling and tethering the ponies we left the grey colts tied to the hedge and went with Elias to look for a suitable field.

" When I was a little one, brother, not so old as Mark,

I've stopped up half the night minding my grandfather's horses," Elias said. " He used to take a deal o' care when he *pooved* his *grys*: I do believe it would have broken the old man's heart to have paid a sovereign for each horse for one night's feed."

" I suppose you had to watch out for the *givengro* [farmer]? " I asked.

" Yes, brother, I had to watch out for the *givengro*. Farmers are cunning devils and if they can catch a horse turned out in their fields they'll lock it up and ask a fabulous ransom. I use to bide there listening, and when I heard anyone about I'd run across the fields in my bare feet and wake up my father and my uncles. Then we would creep back into the field and fetch out the horses."

" I should have thought that the farmer would get them out first."

" No, brother, for most likely he would be spying round on his own. If he found the horses he'd be off back to the farm for his men, and we'd have 'em out and tied up in the lane while he was gone. Sometimes he'd collar one *gry* so that he could ask a ransom for the lot, or maybe he would bring his men with halters ready to slip 'em straight out; but even then I used to run back to the camp in time and if the horses weren't given up quick the *gorgios* had to fight for 'em hard. Keep out from the hedge, brother! It's a bad thing to walk along under a hedge at night. Walk just close enough not to miss an open gate or a gap in the hedge. I only once turned a horse loose in a strange field without looking round the hedge. It was in the winter-time when the cattle is taken in at night, the gates of nine or ten fields had been left open, and my horses walked straight down to the farm, where the farmer jumped out of his bed and locked them up in the stables."

"I expect that taught you to be more careful," I said.

"It did that, brother, for it cost me fifty shillings to get them back." Elias suddenly stopped and kicked against something in the grass. "This field won't do," he said. "There are horses here."

"They may have been taken in for the night," I suggested.

"No, brother," he answered, bending down. "Can't you see the dung is still hot?"

So we returned to the camp, and on the other side of the lane we found a suitable field for the grey colts. Elias covered up the marks of the horses' shoes in the gateway, and we climbed up the steps of our waggon and went to bed.

☙ XVI ❧

AT HALF-PAST FIVE IN THE MORNING I HEARD ELIAS fetching the horses out of the field. It was raw and foggy and the waggon was so comfortable after the little tent in which we had been living that I did not attempt to get up until we were called. I listened to Elias singing as he broke up the wood and prepared the fire, the crackling of the wood and the clank of the kettle as it was hung on the fire-iron. I heard also the peaceful munching of the horses and the occasional brief, vigorous song of a blackbird in the hedge.

Elias had a pleasant, quiet voice and in the early morning, as I afterwards discovered, he used to sit beside the fire with Duke, his brindle greyhound, and sing his favourite songs as he waited for the kettle to boil. He was always up as soon as it was light, and those two hours in which he attended to the horses and boiled the kettle were essentially his; he called no one until he was ready, and no one ever attempted to get up or in any way to disturb his solitude, except Duke, who seemed to have a profound understanding of his master's mood.

This morning as he made the fire he sang an old Irish song. It has a sorrowful and rather beautiful tune to it, made even more impressive by his low-pitched voice.

> Do you think I am a country maid
> To live in sad grief, love and pain
> And for you to roll me in your arms
> Down by the tanyard side?

Red and rosy was her cheeks
And coal-black was her hair,
And nothing were the robes of gold
To what my Irish young girl wore.

If ever I return again
That girl I'll make my bride,
I'll roll her in my arms to-night
Down by the tanyard side.

Travellers have sung this song for years, Elias told us, but it seems as if in each generation a line has been forgotten and in each century a verse. When I meet Elias Ayres I make him sing me that song, for it always reminds me of the first morning that I awoke in the waggon which afterwards carried us so far across England and so deep into the Romany *merripen* [life].

Presently a hissing of steam and a spluttering of the fire shattered the strange early morning peace. Elias came to the foot of our waggon steps and called us, then going to the great tent he banged heavily upon the canvas and shouted: "Leander, get up and give the children their breakfast! Britannia, get yer little sister out of bed! Mark! Rodie! Get up!"

There was a brief stir in the great tent, there were sighs and groans, then once again there was silence. Elias went to the barrel-top waggon and called his father and mother, then observing that no one was moving in the *lue* he returned and banged on the canvas. Again there was a stir, there were sighs and groans, then again a restful silence.

Christopher and I dressed and went down to the fire.

"I see you have lit your fire outside this morning, Elias," said I, sitting down and warming my hands. "It's a raw morning, you must have had a job to find the horses in this mist?"

"I heard their shoes clink together. As you say, it's a raw morning, but when I gets up I always lights the fire outside unless the weather's rough. I wish my woman would hurry up and give the *chavies* their breakfast."

Elias went to the tent and put up such a banging that, after a great deal of angry shouting from within, Leander, his wife, emerged and began cooking the breakfast. When the stir of the woman's rising had died down there followed another silence in the tent, but now the *hobben* was sizzling over the fire, the day had begun and Elias threatened to beat the sleepy ones out of their beds and throw them stark naked out of the *lue*. One by one the children crawled out from under the sackcloth, rising apparently in order of their ages. Britannia, having been routed out, set about dealing with her brother Mark. The tent shook with the ensuing struggle, and then a sleepy, dishevelled Britannia crawled out of the tent and, drawing a stool up to the fire, sat blinking at the flames. Soon afterwards Mark appeared, then Priscilla, and finally Henry and Rodie, the youngest.

We hardly knew whether or not the Ayres wished us to eat at their fire. Christopher and I went up into the waggon and lit the stove, but before we had cooked any food Mrs Ayres, who had been watching us for some time, spoke to Elias. He left his circle and walked up to our waggon.

"What makes you light the stove up there?" said he. "Do you think you are not welcome at my fire?"

I explained that I feared there would not be room for our cooking at the breakfast of so big a family.

"My dear brother," said Elias, "if each of you had a woman and five or six children apiece it would be different. Bring yer *covels* along to the fire and cook what you likes. I don't like to see such *gorgio* ways among travellers."

After we had cooked and finished breakfast Elias said that it was time to start. He fetched the harness, which—in traveller's fashion—was hung on a stick pushed in between the spokes of the wheel and the spring of the waggon; pulled the dog-cart out into the lane and said that he intended to drive Sally. In the excitement of that deal we had failed to mention Sally's great drawback. It was evident that Elias believed the pony to be broken, and when we realized his intention of driving her we were alarmed, both at his likely reaction to the discovery and at the prospect of driving behind her. Christopher said hastily that he would catch her, I went with him, and as soon as we were clear of the camp I asked if he felt sure the pony had never been in harness before the memorable occasion when she threw him out of the waggoner's trap.

"It's difficult to tell," said Christopher. "She was through the garden hedge before I could get a hold on her. She may then have bolted from fright."

We decided to hope for the best, and to tell Elias that we believed her to be a little fresh starting off. After all, it was his own fault for not asking to see her in harness. We caught the pony and returned to the camp, but when Elias, thrusting the collar over the animal's head, said cheerfully, "I'll bet she goes like a flash of lightning!" I did not attempt to reassure him. I had just caught sight of an old and rotten pair of reins, with which our optimistic friend evidently intended to drive Sally. I picked up the bridle and saw that it was in even worse condition.

" You can never drive her in this tackle ! " I said, showing Elias an almost clean break in the reins.

" Why, is she hard-mouthed, brother? "

" I believe she is a little wild starting off," Christopher broke in. " We haven't had her much in harness, but I know she starts off a bit fast."

" So long as she has a good mouth, I cares not how wild she is. Indeed, brother, the more life in 'em the better I likes 'em. But if it pleases you I'll borrow my father's best set of harness."

Elias went to the old man's waggon and shortly returned with a set of black patent leather and white-metal show harness. The breeching, the bridle, and the cribbing were adjusted, and when the pony was put in the trap I held her head while Elias jumped up and took the reins. As I expected, directly she felt the trap move behind she reared up and attempted to plunge forward, in the same way that she had done in the waggoner's garden. Elias checked her on the reins, but he had no sooner brought her to a standstill than she ran backwards until the trap and he disappeared half-way into the hedge. There was a crack from Elias's whip and she plunged back into the lane.

" Jump up ! " he cried. " Let her have her head and she'll be all right ! "

The old people, Leander, and the children stood back, and with the pony plunging and rearing so that the shafts were lifted high into the air we reluctantly jumped up into the trap. For a full minute the animal continued plunging, pawing the air, and backing, then a sharp cut from the whip sent her careering down the lane.

Elias sat well forward on the trap seat, holding the reins in a steady, firm grip, and his hands moved alternatively to and fro as he strengthened his hold on the pony's head. The trap swung from side to side, and breathlessly we sped down the lane at a hard gallop. I was sitting on the outside, and as we approached a deep muddy hollow in the lane I gripped the side of the trap to steady myself. Suddenly Elias glanced round and yelled, " Take yer hand away." I snatched it away, and as the trap bounded over the great rut the iron-bonded wheel shot up between the side of the trap and the splashboard like a huge revolving wood saw.

" My grandmother lost all the fingers of her right hand like that," said Elias.

Gradually the pace slackened, until at last the pony broke out of its gallop into a hard trot. From the moment that Elias had picked up the reins I had felt confidence in his horsemanship; the pony had been going at her hardest gallop, but I was sure that he would have her under control before we reached the main road. It was a good mile from the camp to the highway; we had galloped three-quarters of the distance, and for the remaining quarter of a mile he allowed the pony to hammer along at her fastest trot. From the mouth of the lane we could see that the road was clear on either side, and Elias, without attempting to slacken our pace, turned straight into the highway. Presently he took the reins in one hand and spoke.

" I didn't think she'd be as wild as this," said he.

" It's fortunate you borrowed the old man's harness."
Elias smiled.

" I'm thinking it's fortunate she's a good driver."

" What do you mean by that? " said Christopher.

" I mean this, brother," said Elias. " You didn't tell me
she was green; she's got the makings of a good driver, but
I don't mind telling you that if she'd been a bouncer [a
kicking horse] I shouldn't have felt so friendly towards you,
my brothers." He took a tin of tobacco out of his pocket.
" Hold the reins a minute while I makes myself a cigarette."

I took the reins, but in an instant the pony knew that
she was in different hands. She broke into a gallop, and
when I checked her she drew up so suddenly that she slid
on all four feet.

" You would hardly credit how I picked up a kicking
horse," said Elias as I handed him back the reins. " It was
just after the War. I wanted a good pony to drive out and
get me a living, and I goes and gives all the money I had
in the world for the worst bouncer among the travellers
of these parts. He kicked three bloody traps to pieces in
one week ! "

" How did you come by it? " I inquired, hiding my relief
at the outcome of the previous day's omissions.

" Well, I was stopped in an old grass drove with Leander.
We only had a little rod tent and a donkey and cart, but
we'd saved up a few sovereigns since we'd come together,
and I was looking out for a nice young *gry* [horse]. One
day we is sitting down by the *yog* [fire] drinking a drop of
peeameskie [tea] when a gang of travellers I'd never seen
afore come athwart and *hatches* [stops] agen us in the drove.

They has a fine young five-year-old gelding that takes my eye. I looks at it, I sees they is ready for a bit o' trade and we arranges to drive down to the *kitchimir* [inn] in the evening. Well, they harnesses the *gry* and we all goes to the village, which is six miles away. I tell you, I'd never ridden behind a better horse, and I'm as pleased wi' him in harness as I am wi' his good looks. We has a tidy few drinks. It is in the summer-time, and we is back before dark. Well, brother, for me life I could see nothing wrong wi' the *gry*. They unharnesses it, I starts a-bidding, and we makes a deal afore we *jalls* to *voodrus* [goes to bed]. Early in the morning the travellers wishes us good-bye and starts off for Stratford-on-Avon, where they is going a-pea-picking. They'd seemed civil enough and we promises to meet them at Devizes Fall Fair. Off I goes and buys a pretty little trap, and in the afternoon I puts in the *gry* and he smashes it to pieces. The next day I gets another trap, and after driving him four or five miles he does the same. In one week he smashes up three traps. Well, I gets as I don't care whether I sells him or gives him away. Leander is getting big with the little girl, and I know it's worrying her. Two or three days goes by, then my brother, Ameline, comes along; he had been stopping along wi' these strange travellers and o' corse he tells me what's wrong. That pony had a long silvery tail and would you believe it, brother, when the man was fixing the traces, his wife, the cunning whore of a woman, used to tie the end of its tail to the axle of the trap. She'd tied it with a rope before we'd gone to the *kitchimir*, and with me as innocent as an unborn child she'd untied it when we got back to the camp. Well, as soon as I hears this I gets a bit of rope and does the same. I drives him twenty miles that day, and do you know, true as that pair of reins is in my hand, he's as right as could be, brother."

"And how long did you keep him after that?" I asked.

"Not long, brother, for I had some *rye* in much the same fashion that I was had myself."

After an hour and a half's driving we turned down a lane, at the end of which was a gate leading into the paddock where Elias's friend was encamped. It was a permanent encampment, such as the one from which we had bought Sally, and we understood that the fields on either side of the lane belonged to these horse-dealing Romanies. Two magnificently painted and carved waggons and a large square green tent stood against the hedge to the left of the gate; beyond these were a row of stables, a farrier's shop, three or four hayricks, and a number of traps, carts, and waggonettes.

A small, dark, round-eyed little girl, who was playing with a greyhound at the steps of one of the waggons, stared wonderingly at us as we dismounted from the trap.

"Where is yer father, Cinny?" said Elias, tying the pony to the wheel of a cart.

The little girl's eyes and mouth opened still wider.

"Where is yer Uncle Samson, my dear?" Elias tried again.

The little girl continued to look at us for several moments, then in a clear, small voice she said:

"I'm sure I can't tell you where they is."

"Then go and find yer mother," said Elias.

" She's gone calling."

The little girl rose and with great dignity ascended the waggon steps. Presently she reappeared with an old woman who said that her son, Amos Boswell, had also gone out, but would be back shortly. The old woman showed us the waggons and then discussed family matters with Elias until we heard a horse and trap approaching down the lane. The little girl with the big dark brown eyes opened the gate, and a man driving a smart dog-cart and a handsome skewbald cob turned quickly into the field.

He was the toughest man I had ever seen and I was not surprised when I discovered him to be the first cousin of a famous English heavyweight champion. His features were the most Oriental I have seen among English Romanies; he was not tall, but across his shoulders he was almost as broad as two men, and when he looked at you his eyes seemed to pierce right through you. Elias greeted the man, and introduced us.

" They want a heavy draught-horse, Amos. Summat that'll pull their waggon in the *shillow tem* [North country]; but mind, I wants you to give 'em a *gry* as they'll not be displeased with."

Amos Boswell summoned his two sons, who were approaching across the fields. He then led us round to the stables, where in turn he showed us a dozen or more horses. We saw nothing which took our eyes, and when the last horse had been returned to its stall we told the man of the Eastern face and the broad shoulders that we had seen no horse that we liked well enough to buy.

The man grinned.

"Elias," said he, "you'm brought me two young travellers who is very hard to please."

"Then the sooner you find a *gry* that'll please 'em the better," replied our friend. "If they sees anything they likes they'll buy it, but otherwise they'll not make you a bid."

Amos was thoughtful. "I tell you what," said he at last. "I've one other horse. It's hired out to a farmer two miles from here, but if you mean business I'll send for her."

We asked him to describe the horse.

"It is a six-year-old shire-bred mare. She's got feathers on her feet that long; she's an honest worker, and if I tell you she's fit for the show ring you can mark my words I'll not be telling a lie."

"Has she ever been in a waggon?" I asked.

"You see my brother's waggon there," answered Amos Boswell, pointing to the largest of the two waggons. "God strike me down dead, she pulled it from Southampton in two days. Now if you want to look at her, I'll send after her and you can see her in that waggon for yerself."

An hour later a beautiful bay horse was ridden into the field. It was the first of Mr Boswell's heavy horses really to awaken our interest. The others had been ordinary, nondescript cart-horses, but here was an animal that was, literally, fit for the show ring. She stood sixteen hands two, she had all the appearances of a pure-bred shire, her neck bowed, her chest wide, and her light bay coat shining in the sun like a well-groomed carriage horse. We examined her mouth and her limbs and when we were satisfied that she was no more than six years old, had no side-bones, no wind-galls, nor splints, we asked to see her in harness. Samson Boswell, whose waggon the mare had drawn from Southampton, fetched a magnificent set of gypsy show harness from his tent. The bright white-metal fittings were mounted on brown leather; the shining hames were curled in the true showman's style; there were six ornamental back-straps, a martingale and a bridle decorated with chains, buckles and other ornaments, which years ago, I suppose, were hung on a horse not as decorations, but as protection against the evil spirits who preyed upon the traveller.

The horse, harnessed in this splendour, was put into the waggon. Amos Boswell backed her into the shafts while his son and his brother, Samson, smacked on the traces and buckled up the breeching. From the rapidity with which they did this I began to expect a display of collar-pride on the part of the animal. The waggon had been standing in the same place for several months, the wheels had sunk deep into the ground, and Elias observed that the horse would have a good opportunity of proving her metal. Directly the harness had been adjusted, Amos jerked the bridle and gave a sharp cry of encouragement. The horse sprang forward, leaping and rearing into the collar.

"I don't like that," said Elias in a whisper. "She'll never shift the waggon in that fashion."

The next time the horse reared up and then ran back into the breeching.

"Is she a jibber?" I whispered.

"We'll give her a chance, brother. The waggon's stuck fast and maybe she is only a bit collar-proud."

Again the horse leapt and reared, then suddenly she dug
her feet into the ground and, almost kneeling, put all her
strength into the collar. There was no prancing nor rearing,
the wheels lifted steadily out of the ruts, and the waggon
rolled out into the field. At first she appeared to take some
holding, but after Amos Boswell had made a wide turn in
the field she quietened down and took the waggon through
the gateway without any trouble. It was a steep ascent up
to the road, and at the mouth of the lane there was a sharp
rise turning directly on to the highway. The horse negoti-
ated this with little difficulty, and, once safely on the level,
we all jumped up on the footboard and drove until we
came to a small wayside public-house. We drew up and
ordered our beer to be brought out to us.

" Now if you is going to have any trade," said Elias,
taking a long draught of ale, " get on with it, my brothers ! "

Christopher put down his mug.

" What are you asking for the mare, Mr Boswell? "

" Forty sovereigns I'm asking, young man," replied
Amos Boswell.

" That's too much," I said without hesitation.

" Then make him a bid, my brother," said Elias.

" Thirty pounds," said Christopher after a moment's
thought.

" Talk different to that, young man," rejoined Mr
Boswell. " I'll take thirty-nine sovereigns and no less."

We finished our beer and walked up to the horse.

" That *gry* is growing into money," continued Mr
Boswell, " and wi'out a word of a lie, brother, I tell you
she's an honest mare."

"Thirty-two then," said I, after several minutes' silence. "*Keker* [no]!"

We made another careful examination of the horse, then after standing back and looking at her for a while we bid another pound.

"No, I shan't sell her wi'out I gets what I asks," said Amos Boswell. "I'm not particular whether I sells her or not, so you must please yerselves."

He walked up and down the road thoughtfully, then suddenly he returned and holding out his right hand to us said:

"Quick, brother, thirty-eight sovereigns or nothing?"

There was a second prolonged silence, at the end of which we went up another pound and Mr Boswell came down one.

"Thirty-four and thirty-seven," said Elias, breaking the strained silence. "Look sharp and split the difference!"

Mr Boswell thrust out his right hand again, an expressive gesture.

"Very good, we'll split the difference," said he.

Christopher struck the extended palm, and the deal was clenched. We paid a deposit on the horse, and after arranging to call for it later Amos Boswell turned the waggon and we went back to the camp. The horse held back the great waggon down the steep slope from the road without a drag-shoe or a brake, and in the camp she pushed it back into its original position without any signs of ill-temper. An hour later we climbed up in the trap beside Elias.

"You've made a good deal, my brother," said he, as we swung out of the lane into the main road.

"I believe you are right," I said. "But tell me, why didn't he make more on such a horse?"

"Because she's already earned her money," answered Elias. "Amos bought that mare nearly a year ago. She was on the mowing-machine for two months, then she was hired out for harvesting and ploughing. Now there's little work for her until the hay harvest, but I'll lay a wager she's already earned as much money as you've just paid for her, brother."

On reaching the crossroads below our camp Elias stopped the pony and listened. The encampment lay to our right, but the lane continued across the highway, and it was in this direction that he pointed.

"As we come along the road I thought I could see smoke rising from the far end of that lane," said he. "Listen, brother, I believe there is travellers down there."

I listened and presently I heard the unmistakable noises of a Romany encampment. A dog barked, a horse neighed, and then, faintly, I heard the raised voice of a woman.

Elias turned the pony and we trotted down the rough track until we came in sight of an encampment.

"It's some of the Smallbones' breed," said he. "But I don't think I knows that young fellow in the lane, nor the fair young woman beside him."

We stopped in the camp, and Elias, leaning over the splashboard of the trap, spoke to an oldish man and woman. They were sitting over a wood fire by the steps of a neat red and yellow caravan.

"Well, Father, how is this world treating you?"

" Badly, my son, badly," answered the man. " I'm sick of this dog's life ! "

" And you, Mother? "

" Near the same, Elias," returned the woman. " These is ill-begotten times."

" They is that, Mother, but there is naught but to make the best of 'em. Tell me, where is the boys? "

" They'll soon be here, Elias. We've only just this minute pulled in ourselves. Who are the two young men with you? "

" Strangers to you, Mother. They is stopping along with me. Yesterday they chopped away this pony for my waggon."

" They looks civil enough, Elias. How is the children and the old man and woman? "

" Keeping well, I thank you, Mother."

The young man who had been pitching a rod tent on the other side of the lane left his work and came up to the trap. He looked between the ages of twenty and twenty-three, he was dark and good-looking, his hair was black, and his features were typically Romany. Elias looked at him closely.

" I believe this young traveller is a stranger? " said he.

" He is a stranger to these parts, Elias," said Mr Small-bones. " He is a Smith, his people travel in Surrey and Kent."

" And this fair girl, is she your woman, brother? "

" Yes," answered the young man. " We've only been together a couple of weeks."

" I wish you luck, young man," said Elias. " She's a

fine-looking girl, but she hardly looks like a travelling girl."

" She's not a travelling girl," said the woman beside the fire. " She's a proper *gorgio*! You've never seen such ways!"

" Well, you'm only half a traveller yerself, Mother," replied Elias with a grin.

" If you can't be civil, Elias, you can get on back to where you come from!" retorted the woman angrily.

" All right, Mother, but don't get upsetting the young man and woman. The fellow married where his love lies; I say good-luck to him. Tell me, brother, how do you like this country? Has it changed yer luck?"

" I haven't travelled it long enough to know whether I likes it, nor whether it has changed my luck," said the young Romany.

Elias glanced round at the horses.

" Which is your pony, brother?"

The young man pointed to a young mare colt tethered a little way from the camp. Elias looked at it with surprise.

" Why, it only looks like a yearling," said he. " You've never driven that down from Kent?"

" She's broke in, but I walked her most of the way."

" My dear young man, you'll ruin her!"

" I can't help that," said the boy. " I left the old people without any *vongar* [money]. I can't seem to better myself."

" I tell you what," said Elias. " Drive her down to my *tan* [place] to-night and I'll pay you good money for her. You'll get took if you drive her on the roads any more, my brother."

The young man was thoughtful for a few minutes.

" When shall I come? " he said at last.

" You can come when you please, my brother," said Elias, turning the trap.

Half-way up the lane we met two young men driving a pony and trap in the direction of the camp. They wore handkerchiefs round their necks, their coats were cut in travellers' fashion, but in their features and their looks there was little of the true Romany. Elias stopped the pony and spoke to the young men. They answered him in a way that was outwardly friendly, but which I thought lacked the comradeship of the true Romany.

" A cunning half-caste lot that ! " said Elias, as we crossed over the main road. " Never have anything to do with them, my friends; they'd do you down as quick as they'd do down their own mother and father. They come from a bad breed."

" The two in the trap looked much alike. Are they brothers? " I asked.

" No, they are cousins," answered Elias. " The one driving is Tom Smallbones' boy. The younger one is the son of Tom's brother. And the stranger in the lane is a fool to take his young wife into their bloody company."

❧ XVII ❧

An hour before dark the rumbling of a.trap brought us from the *lue*, where for the past two hours we had been smoking and talking beside a warm fire.

We waited and in a few minutes the young Romany from Kent, followed by the two cousins in a second trap, drove into the camp and dismounted. Elias greeted them and proceeded to examine the yearling colt.

" Jump in and drive her up and down the lane, my boy," said he, after he had looked at her mouth and felt her legs.

The young man climbed into the trap, and cracking his whip drove rapidly up and down. Except for a slight fidgeting of the head the colt appeared to be perfectly broken; it turned in the narrow lane like a horse broken longer than it had lived, and as it tore past us it answered the reins quickly and without hesitation. Presently he jumped down, gripped one of the trap wheels and, signalling for me to do likewise, cracked his whip. The pony sprang into the collar and, nearly wrenching off my arm, dragged the trap and the locked wheels along the lane.

Elias watched in silence and when the young man had finished showing off the colt's qualities he asked the price.

" Will you make me a bid? " said the young Gypsy, after a moment's consideration.

"No, I can't be both buyer and seller. What is yer price?"

"Six guineas I'm asking."

"I'll give you five pounds."

"No, but I'll split the difference with you."

"Five pounds is my price. Take it or leave it, young man."

"Then five pounds it is!"

The young Romany struck Elias's outstretched hand, and the most rapid deal that I have witnessed in a Gypsy camp was closed. Elias paid out five pound-notes and in return received a shilling luck money. We then went into the *lue*, and for an hour sat beside the fire and listened to the young man talk of the Surrey heaths, the green lanes of Kent, and the great yearly meeting of the travellers on Epsom Downs. When he had finished he asked Elias and us to accompany him to the public-house in the village.

"We'll walk down later on, brother," said Elias. "But take my advice and run yer trap back to the camp. No doubt either Pat or Christopher will go with you and look after the colt."

I rose and went outside. The trap lamps were lit and we drove down the lane until we came to the Smallbones' camp. The handsome fair girl was sitting over a fire outside her tent, and when we arrived she jumped up and helped unharness the pony.

"I sold the colt," said the young man to his wife.

"Did you get much?"

"I did, I got five pounds—which is more than I hoped to get, Ann."

" And when will you get another pony to take the things about? " asked the girl.

" As soon as I can, but for the time being we can tie the cart on behind the waggon."

He took out the five pound-notes and handed them to the girl.

" You had better take care of the money," said he.

" I had not," replied the girl. "It's not my place to look after the money, and in any case I have no safe place to keep it."

The young man hesitated and then returned the notes to his pocket. He finished unharnessing the colt and presently we returned down the lane. On the crossroads I saw the cousins' trap approaching. I waited and when the young man had jumped up I led the colt back to the camp.

Inside the *lue* I found Christopher working on a drawing of the boy Mark. Eight candles burnt merrily in the great tent, and although they delighted little Rodie the women and the older children were deeply concerned at such unheard-of extravagance. I sat down beside the fire and spent the evening talking, smoking, and playing with the children. On a winter's night there is nothing pleasanter than a seat beside a wood fire in the *lue* of a cheerful Gypsy family. The Ayres were very intrigued with Christopher's ' scribings,' as indeed all Gypsies are with any form of art or craft. Leander Ayres and Priscilla sat for him, and at half-past nine, when the last of the candles had gutted out, we walked down to the village with Elias.

The cousins' pony and trap was not, as we had expected, outside the inn, and on entering we were told that the landlady had refused to continue serving the young men, who had driven on to the public-house in the next village. Elias called the old woman and asked why she had refused them.

" Because the boy with the dark hair had drunk more than was good for himself or his pocket," said she. " He didn't know what he was doing or saying. And the other young fellows what was with him were trying their level best to make him worse! "

" Did he spend much money, Mother? " said Elias.

" He did, but it's not for me to tell you what he spent."

" I know what he had, Mother, for I've a-just paid him good money. You'll do no harm by telling me what he spent."

" Well, if you wants to know," said the old woman at last, " he spent three sovereigns."

" Three sovereigns! " exclaimed Elias, under his breath. " But tell me, Mother, did the other young fellows spend anything? "

" Not a farthing! They had what they wanted out of the boy. He got in such a state that he threw his money about on the floor and kept treating every one in this here room. Now do you know all you want? "

" Yes, Mother, and I thank you," said Elias.

I ordered three pints of ale and we sat down in a corner beside the fire.

" God take my breath! If I'd known what was a-coming I'd never have given that young fool five pounds for his colt."

" I didn't tell you that he took out the money and asked his wife to look after it," I said.

" No, brother, you never told me that. "

" I saw him offer her the five notes when I went to fetch back the colt. She refused to take them and said that it was his place to look after the money."

" Then she has her own self to blame," said Elias. " She's a fine-looking wench, but she's a *gorgio* and she doesn't understand the ways of travellers. As I told you yesterday, beside this same fire, a travelling man is a fool wi' money and it takes a travelling girl to understand him."

As we left the inn at ten o'clock Elias spoke:

" We will walk home slowly, for I should like them to catch us up afore we reaches the crossroads."

When we had passed the last house in the village we ambled slowly along the lane until we heard the trotting of a horse and the rattle of trap wheels in the distance. We halted, and presently a pair of lights appeared some two hundred yards behind us. The horse had been trotting fast, but now it slowed down and we heard voices which, as the trap approached, grew louder and apparently more angry. At last the animal stopped altogether. There was a burst of drunken, angry, indistinct voices, then a loud crack of a whip, a clatter of hoofs, and the horse broke into violent gallop. Elias leapt into the road and shouted, but the trap tore past us and disappeared round a bend in the lane.

We walked on quickly for several minutes, then, pausing to listen, we heard the horse slow down again.

" If we hurry we'll overtake them," said Elias breaking into a run.

We followed and before long the red rear lights of the trap came into sight. The pony had stopped, but instead of the previous shouting and cursing the noise of a great struggle came from the trap. We ran hard, but before we could reach the spot we heard the thud of a man falling heavily to the ground. The whip cracked and the pony galloped away.

As we arrived the dark young man, holding his hands to his face, staggered up.

" The bastards! The poxy bastards! " he mumbled.

He had obviously been drinking heavily, but he had pulled himself together and was now fully aware of his surroundings. Elias gripped him by the arm, and when the boy uncovered his face I saw a great gash across his forehead.

" Why did they throw you out? " cried Elias.

" Because they want to get at my girl," he shouted. " They're roaring drunk, and if they get back first they'll have her out of the tent and do what they like with her! The bleeding dogs are all against me! "

He broke furiously from Elias.

" I'll hang for 'em both if they soil her with their vile carcases! "

Elias followed him without hesitating.

"Across the fields! " he yelled after the boy. " We can be there as quick as the pony! "

He scrambled through the hedge on the left; the three of us followed and together ran across the fields, over ditches, bogs, and the uneven furrows of ploughed land. Presently in the distance we saw the lights of the trap moving down the track below the Smallbones' camp. In a few minutes we scrambled breathlessly into the lane. The trap was now ahead out of sight, but stumbling through the mud we hurried on till at last a dim light showed in the camp. The young Gypsy had been in front all the time, but now he disappeared and ahead I could hear the girl screaming for him.

We reached the camp just behind him. He had attacked the eldest cousin and was now tearing him savagely from the terrified girl. Elias went to his assistance, while Christopher attacked the second cousin, who, too drunk to put up a fight, fell with a thud to the ground.

The girl's clothing had been torn in the struggle, but it was evident that she had not been wronged. The young man, despite his winded condition and the bleeding wound in his forehead, was intent on finishing the fight single-handed; he and the cousin were equally matched in size and age, both had drunk heavily, both had sobered, and as neither of the old people came from the waggon to interfere Elias stood out and together we watched the two men fight.

" They is bound to settle it between them sooner or later," said Elias.

Gradually the young Romany drove his opponent against the hedge; the blows from his hard fists resounded upon the other's face and body until, after five minutes' hard fighting, the cousin doubled up and sprawled on the ground.

Unfortunately the young man's troubles did not end with the fight, for after we had gone his wife discovered that only seventeen shillings out of the five pounds remained.

The next morning Elias was up earlier than usual. We breakfasted at half-past six and then walked up the lane with the intention of bringing the unfortunate young Romany and his *gorgio* bride back to our place. When we reached the encampment, however, we found only the Smallbones' waggons and tents; the two had gone, and the only proof of their ever having been there was a round patch of ashes in the grass on the other side of the lane. The two cousins were not about, but the old man and woman were sitting beside a fire, and their sour, black looks (particularly those of the woman) were full of hatred and resentment.

"When did the young fellow and his wife go?" said Elias sharply.

The old man and woman did not answer.

"I asked you when the young fellow went?" repeated Elias angrily.

The old woman stirred the fire and without removing her gaze said:

"Is it any business of yours when they went?"

"After the way you and yer breed treated the young fellow I'm a-going to make it my business!"

"As soon as I got up this morning I told them to clear out. A-quarrelling and fighting they've been all night. They've been a bloody trouble to us ever since we joined in with their unlucky company. Now take yer bodyguard and go on back to yer own place, for I tell you straight, Elias, I don't want you here meddling with my affairs!"

"It's not with your affairs I'm concerned, Mother; it's the way yer rotten breed flung that young fellow out of the cart last night and then tried to ruin his girl for him."

"You'll get yerself took up if you talks like that, Elias. What does my son want with a *pawno muied* [pale-faced] whore of a *gorgio* girl?"

" What many a man had with you afore you had yer own man! Tell me, when did the young fellow go? "

" Get out of my place, you lying, devilish man! They went off an hour ago, he pulling the trap and she crying her silly eyes out because the fool had spent all the money he took for the colt! Now take yerself off afore I throw this kettle of boiling water over you! "

When we departed down the lane Elias gave vent to his anger and his distress at the plight of the unfortunate couple.

" I hate to think of them poor devils on the road without a horse in their cart and without money in their pockets. I think I shall harness the pony and look for 'em. They couldn't have gone far."

Fifteen minutes later we left the camp in the trap, with a spare pony tied on behind. We made inquiries in the village and then drove for several miles along a road which they were said to have taken. Further inquiries led us from village to village in one direction after another, and after a long morning's search we found them eating their dinner under a hedge by the roadside. Elias jumped out of the trap.

" Why did you not come up to my place this morning? " said he. " If I had known what was in your mind I'd have made you move last night."

The young man said nothing.

" It upset me when I found you gone," went on Elias. " Indeed, brother, I couldn't rest when I thought of you pulling this trap without so much as a sovereign left out of the money I give you for the colt. Why did you let 'em rob you like that, brother? "

Still the young man remained silent.

"And you, young woman," continued Elias, turning to the girl. "How is it you didn't know better than to refuse the money yer man offered you? I can see the trouble with you two young ones. You, my dear, have never known what it is to earn a living on the roads. You is not used to travellers' ways, and what this young man wants is a woman who can break him in. He is like a colt and you don't know how to put him in harness. I'm telling you the truth! Once you gets to the bottom you'll never again get up. You two is nearly at the bottom, and if you don't mind what you'm about you'll be spending the rest of yer days sleeping under a bit of sacking and pushing yer things about in a perambulator with only three wheels on."

The two gazed silently into the dying embers of the fire and after a moment's pause Elias went on again.

"If you come back with me I'll give you the chance to get yourself another *gry*. I can see you've both had a bad start and I'm a-going to see you righted. Your girl shall go out hawking with my woman, and I'll take you with me if I can get a job on the fields for a couple of weeks. I knows you is a stranger to these parts, but you ought never to have got in with the company you've just left."

The girl put a hand on the young man's shoulder. Presently he rose and harnessed the pony which we had brought with us. The girl packed her belongings in their trap and we drove back to camp, where the young couple pitched their tent in the lane a hundred yards below our waggon. The next morning Elias found a job on the mangel fields of a near-by farm; the pay was thirty-three shillings a week and an additional eight or nine shillings for overtime.

ROMANY BOY

At seven o'clock the morning following, he and the young man from Kent started work, and the fair girl, carrying a basket of pegs which her husband had made the previous night, accompanied Granny and Leander to the neighbouring villages.

❧ XVIII ❧

O<small>N A BRILLIANT SPRING MORNING IN THE BEGINNING OF</small> April three weeks after we had left the hill of the pine-trees, Elias awakened us before his ritual beside the fire was over.

Outside the great shire-horse, tied to one of the back wheels, rubbed her nose and rocked the newly painted waggon from side to side, so that the glistening harness, which yesterday had been the prided possession of Mr Amos Boswell, slipped from a hook and crashed to the floor.

Last night we had returned from the Boswells' camp with the horse and the show harness, which in a moment of rashness we bought with the remainder of our capital. It had cost us fourteen pounds, but, as Amos had observed, the harness was the only thing we required to make ourselves the owners of the prettiest turn-out in the West of England. For the last fortnight we had been working from early in the morning until late at night. We had burnt off the old paint with blow lamps, smoothed down the woodwork, re-painted and lined out the wheels, the carvings, and the undercarriage in gold, red, green, yellow, and blue. The wheelwright in the village had made us two new wheels, and there had been an entertaining afternoon in the black-smith's yard when our wheels and some forty others had been bonded over an immense wood fire. It had been a regular festival of bonding. For a week a carpenter had arrived in the camp every morning and until five o'clock at night worked on our waggon, renewing all the broken and rotten parts. New springs had been fitted, new axle-cases, new window-frames, and now on this spring morning the waggon looked just as it must have looked when, fifty-nine years ago, it left Boltern's yard in Reading.

When I opened the door and went down the waggon steps the great tent was no longer standing majestically in the lane, for the tall ash-poles which had supported it during the winter months had been burnt on the camp-fire the night before. The spring had come, and there would no longer be need for anything but small rod tents in which to lie at night. So the *lue* had been pulled down, the canvas had been packed away in the carts, and the framework had been burnt on the fire around which we had spent our last evening with Elias and his family.

It had been a merry and yet a sad evening, for at times I had looked into the fire and wondered how much I would miss being tormented by the mischievous Priscilla and the dark-eyed Rodie. To-morrow, I thought, I would no longer be helping Mark train his pony to jump, nor teaching the children to spell so that they could read the *pukkering cosh-ties* [signposts]. I would no longer be tempted to put my arms round the beautiful Britannia when I met her carrying water back from the spring on a dark night. I would no longer hear Elias singing in the early morning, nor would he be with us to walk to the village inn, or on a moonlit night to take us rabbiting with the greyhound, Duke. There would no longer be Leander, with her fortune-tellings, her weird stories, and her firm belief in the doctrine of love and hate—both of which she gave her husband in an unlimited degree. I would miss Granny and Grandfather with their tales of the golden age, and it would seem strange without the children's bantams strutting about the camp or flapping boldly through the windows of our waggon.

But in spite of these pleasant, if sad, reflections, it had been a delightful evening. On our return from the Boswells' camp we had driven down to the White Hart, where, with the money provided by Grandfather, Elias, and ourselves, we had purchased three cases of bottled beer and stout. Leander had cut up the poles of the discarded *lue*, and round a blazing fire in the middle of the lane we had celebrated our stay together. Mark had played step-dances and Irish jigs on his melodeon, while his father had danced on the seat board of a trap flung down beside the fire. Britannia had removed her shoes and stockings and, rather shyly at first, danced an Irish jig. Then Grandfather had followed with a step-dance.

" Double time ! " Leander had shouted. " Double time !"

Tum-tum a-diddly tump, p-tump tump tump! thumped the melodeon.

The young Gypsy from Kent was persuaded to go on the board.

" Lancashire time, my boy ! " cried Grandfather. And Lancashire time it was !

In the firelight we had watched them dance, then settling down on the stools and the boxes beside the fire we had talked, drunk, and sung until far into the night. The fire had crackled and the horses had munched around us.

And so early the next morning we packed and harnessed

our horses in the April sunshine. We intended to go to Yorkshire, and Elias was going to Dorset, where his brother Daniel was encamped on a desolate common with two young children and a wife who gave him every reason to expect a third. The waggons and traps jolted down the rough lane; the children ran along on either side; the dogs followed at the wheels; and the bantams, hung in boxes below the axles, cackled with alarm.

On the crossroads we shook hands with Elias and his wife, the old man and woman, the children, and the young Romany from Kent. We watched the waggons and traps until they were out of sight, then Christopher took the horse by the bridle and the waggon rumbled easily along the hard road.

Three miles past the village we reached the foot of a long, steep hill. It was the first really bad hill we had come upon, and until we ascended it we had little idea of the gradient on which the horse would be able to manage the waggon. We pulled up at the bottom, but Christopher had as much as he could do to hold the horse and stop her from rushing at the hill, while I searched for a big stone with which to block up the waggon. A hill to Sally—the new horse, round and healthy in appearance, named after her predecessor —was like a bone to a dog. Leading her on the gravel which had been washed in to the side of the road we went up the first part of the hill, then blocking up one of the wheels we made her rest. Farther up the gravel had been completely washed away, and it was necessary to turn the waggon from one side of the road to the other in order to make the ascent possible.

When we reached the top of the hill the horse was dripping with sweat, and pulling up in a gateway we let her rest for a quarter of an hour. I lit a cigarette and leaning over the gate looked down on the flat fields, which stretched from the foot of the hill as far as Salisbury Plain and the Marlborough Downs. The grass had not yet lost its winter greyness, but even from a distance the buds showed up in the hedges and trees and made the dark branches look as if they were dripping with a bright green dew.

During the early morning the sky had been cloudless, but now low black clouds appeared on our left and there were heavy showers of rain and gusts of wind. The sun shone in between the showers, and it was a typical April day.

When we started down the other side of the hill we did not make use of the drag-shoe, and before we had gone more than a hundred yards the brake lever broke away from the side of the waggon, and all the weight was thrown on the horse. Fortunately we were close to the side of the road and were able to get the wheels cutting into the bank before the horse fell or bolted. It was this accident that made us slightly change our route in order to have the brake repaired at Devizes. We took the first road in that direction, and when we began to feel hungry I boiled the kettle on the stove and prepared a meal. At half-past one we pulled down a narrow lane and hitched out the horse just before a heavy shower of rain beat on the roof. It was the first time we had stopped in a fresh place with the waggon, and we looked out of the windows on a fresh scene.

In the afternoon we travelled along a winding road running a mile or two from the foot of the downs. The country, just here, was well cultivated; the green wheat stood nearly a foot high, and the small leaves of the mangels and beans were beginning to appear above the chalky soil. There were no hedges; the road sometimes ran on a level with the fields and sometimes between steep, loose chalk banks. The pee-wits, twisting and turning about in the air, excitedly followed us. As they darted directly overhead, their wings beating audibly, they anxiously watched their nests and the movements of Nell, slinking along the fields to the rear of the waggon. Clouds gathered in the sky; the sun, half disappearing, sent dark shadows racing across the wheat fields. A gust of wind shook the waggon, rain and hail swept almost horizontally across the road, and when the sun reappeared there was a mixed smell of wet chalky earth and steam which rose from the horse's back. As I walked along beside the waggon I had to shield my eyes from the sudden glare of the sun reflected on the drenched wheat.

It was nearly dark when we stopped outside a public-house four miles from Devizes. A workman in the bar told us of a grass lane three miles this side of the town.

" I expect there will be several caravans up there to-morrow night," he said when he had explained the exact position of the lane.

" Why to-morrow night? " I asked.

" The Spring Fair is in two days."

" Devizes Spring Fair ! "

" I would have sworn that you were on your way to it."

" We had forgotten that it was so near, but now that we are here we shall certainly stop."

" I saw five or six encampments on the Bath road when

I was coming back from work to-night," the man said. " They generally bide in the lanes ten or twelve miles from the town and close in the night before the Fair when it is too late for the police to shift 'em."

" What are the Devizes police like? "

" The Superintendent is all right and as far as I know the constables are all right, but if you stay in the lane too long some interfering bastard is sure to report you. Your horse has got a long pull in front of it. The hill up to the town is over two miles long."

" Devizes must be very high up."

" They say there's no town in the West of England like it. It is over five hundred feet above sea level and it stands on a jut of land which stretches out from the downs. The hills, however, shouldn't worry you with a horse like that."

We bought some candles from the landlord, and after lighting the lamps we started in the direction of the camping lane. Two or three miles from the town we found a grass track leading to some fields about a hundred and fifty yards away from the road. There were fireplaces on either side of the lane, and presuming it to be the place of which the man had spoken we drew in the waggon and unhitched the horse. When we had unharnessed and tied the horse up to a wheel I blew out the candles and left Christopher to mix up a feed of oats and chaff for the horse while I lit the oil lamp and prepared supper in the waggon. Motor-cars and bicycles and pedestrians passed up and down the main road, but no one disturbed us in the lane. We made our beds under the waggon, and before turning in for the night tied a chain across the lane and let the horse loose.

After breakfast the next morning we took the caravan to a blacksmith in Devizes. We pulled the van into the smith's yard and arranged to have the horse shod and the brake repaired. Three heavy horses were in the shop waiting their turn, but fortunately all the shoes were prepared and the blacksmiths were young and agile. By half-past eleven Sally was tied up in the smithy and the work on the waggon was started.

While the horses were being shod I noticed that numbers of dogs slinked into the smithy and picked up pieces of horse hoof, which they carried into the yard and devoured.

" Why do they eat that? " I asked as I worked the bellows and watched the procession of dogs enter the shop and scavenge among the bits and pieces on the floor.

The blacksmith wrestled with Sally until he got one of her hind legs between his knees, and Nell stood solemnly watching the activities of the preoccupied Devizes dogs.

" I'll warrant," said the blacksmith, " that a bit of horse hoof is the finest thing there is for a dog's blood. Hold still, my pretty gal! Do you notice how the coats of all these dogs shine? "

I had been thinking that some of the dogs were the most mangy, starved, wasted, dissipated-looking dogs that I had ever seen, but I said nothing because the blacksmith's lurcher looked extremely healthy, and it suddenly occurred to me that some of these decrepit animals might have nothing else but horse hoof on which to live and love.

" The dogs come here every day from all parts of the town," went on the blacksmith. " A rich old lady sends the maid here with her Pekinese."

I picked up a piece of hoof and offered it to Nell, but she refused to touch it and I was forced to the conclusion that it must be an acquired taste.

The smithy, like most buildings of its kind, was very old. There were no modern improvements; the roof, the beams, and the forge chimney were covered with inches of dust and soot; and the ash handle of the old calf-skin bellows was worn to a fine spindle by the hands of past blacksmiths and travellers who, like ourselves, looked after the forge while their horses were being shod. I watched the smith and I was struck by the fact that he never so much as marked the outside of the hoof with his file. The ruthless filing down of the hoof had always been a source of irritation to me and presently I asked him why he took such trouble to make the shoes fit perfectly.

" During the War I was shoeing in France," he said, " and I was taught not to file the hoof because there is said to be a film of natural oil just under the surface. The rule in the Army was to make the shoe fit the horse instead of the horse fit the shoe."

When the two blacksmiths went away for their dinner we boiled our kettle and cooked our lunch on the forge, and it was four o'clock in the afternoon when the new brake lever was completed and bolted on the waggon. In the town we had bought provisions, a sack of oats, and a sack of coal, which we had stowed on the rack at the back of the waggon. After paying the blacksmith we returned to the lane in which we had camped the previous night.

It was a fine, warm evening and we made the fire beside the hedge and had supper outside. The sun set and cast a red shimmering light on the tops of the trees and the roof of the waggon. During the twilight that followed there was a lull in the traffic on the main road, and for a while the silence was only broken by the low cry of a moorhen as it splashed across a near-by pond and the steady, peaceful munching of the horse. We lay on the grass and smoked and talked until we heard the sound of horses on the road below. I stood up and listened, and when I was able to distinguish the light clatter of ponies, the heavier clatter of cart-horses, and the rattle of loose-shaking wheels I knew that it was travellers on their way to the Fair. There was a great deal of stopping, shouting, and talking as the horses ascended the hill.

Standing on the bank we were able to look over the hedge and see the main road for several hundred yards below the mouth of the lane. Presently a waggon lighted only by one lamp appeared. A trap driven by two small children followed; then a second waggon followed by a boy mounted on a cart colt. In a few minutes a third waggon drawn by a pair of horses abreast appeared, then a waggonette, a pony tied on behind, and a second trap. We could hear more horses coming up the hill, but by this time the first caravan had turned into the lane. Christopher caught Sally and tied her up to a gate.

The pony and trap turned in after the waggon, the two children each tugging determinedly at a rein so that I expected to see the trap turn over in the ditch at the mouth of the lane. As the waggons and carts drew off the road the men and women looked at us and our encampment with a mixture of surprise and suspicion. They spoke quickly to each other and turning round called out to those in the road.

Directly the first waggon reached our camp the men and women behind left their own vehicles and collected round us. They were anxious to find out who we were, and we were equally anxious to discover whether they resented our presence in a lane that barely had room for us all. The string of waggons and traps and horses extended from our encampment to the lane end and for some distance down the road. Altogether there were five caravans, seven or eight traps, and between twenty and thirty horses.

" You're on the road late to-night, Grandfather," I said, addressing a tall old man who had been driving the first waggon. He carried a silver-mounted whalebone whip in his hand, he had thick white side-whiskers brushed forward so that they protruded from his face like horns; he wore a black trilby hat pushed up in the middle, and smoked a short clay pipe.

" You're right, my son," he replied. " It's a fool's game being on the roads when the lights of the motor-cars dazzle your eyes and you don't know whether you be in the ditch or over the hedge. My eyesight is not very good. Tell me, my son, do you know me or don't you? "

" I can see they be strangers without you asking them, my man," said an old woman, looking out of the window of the waggon. " You've never seen any of us before? "

I had a recollection of having seen the wife of the man with the second waggon, but I could not remember where and I did not refer to it.

" No," I said, " we haven't been travelling in this part of the country for long."

" Have your *raklies jalled* to *voodrus*? [Have your women gone to bed?] " asked the woman from the second waggon.

" What, you've got no women? "

There was a stir. There were exclamations of surprise from the old man with the protruding side-whiskers down to the children who had been arguing in the trap. I could not, however, discern whether they were uttered out of pity or admiration. They looked up at our waggon, then they looked at us and seemed to demand an explanation. We told them that we had no parents. The more reason then that we should each have a woman of our own. I pointed out that I would enjoy, as well as any man, having a woman of my own, and that I hoped—and had hoped for some time—one day to prove my genuine affection for the sex. The old man with the side-whiskers said that he admired my principles, the others smiled and there was less distrust in their dark faces.

" And how long have you been stopping here, young man? " asked the traveller who had been driving the waggon and the pair of horses. " The *kitchimengro opray* the *chumbo pukkered mandi* a *gry* and *verdo awved akkoi* last *rarti* [The public-house man on the hill told me that a horse and waggon came there last night]."

" He *penned* [said] that it was foreign Romanies," remarked the woman from the second waggon.

" No," said Christopher, " we stopped at the public-house last night. I've seen no foreign travellers about here."

The candle in the lamp of the first caravan flickered and guttered out. There appeared to be an argument going on among the travellers whose waggons were still out in the road. Those with whom we had been talking disappeared, and the old man after cursing the lamp followed them down the lane. " Let's go and see what's on with the people," he said as he limped off, pushing his way between the carts and horses and the hedge. " Let's go and see what's on, my son. Mind that bloody bouncing horse don't kick out at you ! "

When we reached the mouth of the lane we found one of the waggons half turned over in the ditch. The frightened horse was rearing and snorting in the grip of an infuriated man, an equally frightened woman with a baby was clambering out of the waggon, several men hung on to the side, while others ran to their carts for ropes. Suddenly there were shouts from the road as an unattended pony wandered out in front of an approaching car.

" Get out on the road and mind those bleeding ponies, will you? " the owner of the waggon shouted as he struggled to prevent the van horse from letting the waggon back into the ditch.

Ropes were thrown over the roof of the waggon and secured on the leaning side. Christopher and I and the old man seized them, the men and boys pushed on the wheels, turning them inch by inch until the waggon was out of the ditch. Directly the ropes were detached the owner swung the horse round and faced the waggon to the road.

" What have you done that for, my brother? " cried the old man with surprise.

The man ignored him, and bringing the horse to a standstill turned to the woman with the baby.

" Get up inside unless you're going to walk ! " he

shouted. "Girl! Get up in that trap! Gus and Kenza, bring on the waggon and the horses!"

The old man grabbed him by the arm and repeated his question.

"What do you think I'm going to do, Liberty? Light my fire and bide out in the road all night? Jesus Christ, is there room to tie a horse up in the lane, Liberty? What dog's flesh do you think I'm made of? I wondered why you were all in such a hurry to get up the hill. Why didn't you pull right up the lane and let me in? I like to tell a man the rights of my mind. Do you think I'm a-going to bide in this lane—packed in like a lot of bloody pigs, herded in like——"

"Talk sense, brother," cried the old man, "couldn't you see the young fellow's waggon up there? If you hadn't 'a' tried to back out of the lane you wouldn't have had the waggon in the ditch—speak the truth!"

The man cracked his whip and started up the hill.

"You bloody toad!" shouted the woman with the baby. "I'll beat yer brains in with the kettle iron when I catch up with you! Isn't the lane free to the young travellers? You wait till I catch up with you! You want to go to the next public—that's what you want to do! You only thinks of yer own guts. Cursed, bloody man, stop that waggon!"

Holding the baby in one arm she shook her fist, shouted, and followed up the road. I was the only one, I think, who noticed that the waggon had no lights. The girl who had been instructed to attend to the straying pony reluctantly took the bridle and led the pony and trap up the hill. In a few moments the last caravan and a boy leading a pair of horses followed. When they had disappeared the Gypsy from the third waggon turned to us.

"That is a strange, jealous-minded man," he said. "As soon as he found that there was strangers in the lane he wouldn't stop. He is *trashed* [frightened] that some one will run away with his woman. What can you do with such a man, brother?"

"What makes him like it?" I asked.

"Well, young man, he and his woman hadn't been together but two weeks when he was called out to France. He was buried twice and then took prisoner. The Germans had him for two years and he began to think that his little woman would find herself another man. Two years is a long time for a man to have a thing like that on his mind. She waited for him, brother, but when he got back to her there wasn't a young travelling fellow who come near the place but he didn't think he slept wi' her at one time or another. It was a wonder he didn't commit a hundred murders."

"He'll camp in Ashe Lane to-night," said another man. "When we meet him at the Fair he'll drink wi' us and behave like every other true-blooded travelling man. Pull yer waggon on, Father, and let's get the horses out."

The travellers gave us an immense iron kettle to boil on our fire while they were arranging their camps. After filling it with a bucket of water and lending them our hurricane lamp we sat by our fire and watched the waggons being shifted into place. The first two waggons were pulled up the lane beyond our encampment. The horses were taken out and stood in the lane grazing or resting, the dim light of the lamps shining on their harness and their gleaming

ROMANY GIRL

coats. Candles were lighted in the waggons; the tent rods were taken out of the carts, pushed into the ground, fastened by the ridge pole, and covered by odd pieces of canvas and sacking. The harness was taken off the horses and was hung up or thrown under the carts; smoke rose from the waggon chimneys; women and girls carried bundles of blankets and straw into the tents. When the work was finished and the dogs tied up to wheels and axles, the man from the second waggon removed the lamps from his carts and waggon and hid them in the hedge.

" I always *garrav* the *duds* [hide the lamps], young man," he remarked, looking critically up at our lamps. " The *muskero* [policeman] cannot shift you when you've got no lamps. To tell you the truth, I would like to see you put yours out of the way."

When Christopher had hidden the lamps I informed the travellers that the kettle was boiling, and one by one the men and women and children came up to the fire and sat down on the grass. Twenty-eight people crowded round the fire, and when the sticks blazed up the light shone on a sea of dark, curious faces. The woman whom I thought I recognized made a large pot of tea while the men and the other women fried meat and bread. The children, instead of anxiously watching their parents preparing the food, stared solemnly at us or peered curiously up into the waggon. Our oil lamp blazing wastefully on the table appeared to fascinate them. They accepted their food without fighting for it, and ate it without looking at it.

When the crocks had been packed away in the hampers the men brought out tins of fine, black shag, and, after taking out sufficient to roll a cigarette, passed them on to their wives and children.

" Have you ever travelled with Elias Ayres? " I asked, lighting a cigarette and handing the firebrand on to the old man with the side-whiskers.

" Elias Ayres? " repeated the man from the second waggon. " That is my brother-in-law. My woman and his woman is true sisters."

" Ah, that is who she reminds me of! " I said. " When I was sitting by the fire waiting for the kettle to boil I was trying to think where I had seen her. Leander and your wife are very much alike."

" They are as alike as two white gate-posts," replied the man. " When did you last see my brother-in-law? "

" Yesterday morning. We have been stopping with him for the last three or four weeks. We chopped with him for this waggon."

This information immediately removed the slightly mistrustful attitude of the travellers. They afterwards told us that they had suspected us to be foreign travellers who were pretending to be natives of the country. At first, they said, they had been unable to account for our difference in speech, our flash waggon, horse and harness, and our celibate lives.

There was a stir of excitement.

" Why didn't Elias come to the Fair with you? " said the man from the second waggon.

" He had a letter from his brother, who is travelling in Dorset."

" That's right, young man, his brother Daniel Ayres travels that country. What did the letter say? "

" It said that his wife was in the family way and that they were stopping by themselves on a common near Dorchester. Elias started off yesterday morning."

" I should have thought that he'd have come to the Fair with you first. I've never before known Elias miss the Spring Fair."

" God Almighty, Arthur ! " exclaimed Leander's sister. " How could the man go to Fair when his brother is out on a lone common and the woman is likely to have her *chavie* at any minute of the day ? They is stopped in a lonely place —the nearest house is three miles away—and there isn't a child old enough to take care of the woman while Daniel drives the pony to the doctor's place. Talk sense, my dear man ! "

" Did the old man and woman go down the country with them ? " asked the old Romany with the side-whiskers, removing his pipe and spitting into the fire. When I had answered he explained that his name was Loveridge and that Elias's mother was his sister. The men from the second and third waggon were his two sons, Arthur and German.

" And tell me," continued old Mr Loveridge, " did Elias take any waggons with him ? "

" He had one which he took down for his brother's wife."

" Now if he thinks Melisa is going up in a waggon he's wrong. I knows the young woman better than Elias. If she don't have her baby down on the ground "—here the woman pressed the palm of her hand lovingly on to the earth— " she won't have it at all—God bless her true Gypsy heart ! "

" Did you see any of the Smallbones when you was along wi' Elias ? "

243

"We saw as much as we ever want to see of them," I said.

Christopher gave an account of the affair with Tom Smallbones and the *gorgio* bride. The story immediately held their attention, and when he had finished a young man, who had been the last to pull in the lane, told us of an occasion when his wife had had cause to knock Tom Smallbones over the top of the head with a kettle iron and he had fought him outside a public-house in Westbury. The young man who spoke was the roughest-looking Romany I had ever seen in my life. His long, unkempt, black hair stuck out from under his soiled cap; his face was unshaven, the stubble thick and black; his steely eyes glistened and his moustache was wide and ferocious. The girl who sat beside him looked as placid and gentle as he looked virile and wild. She was only nineteen, and the child that slept in her arms was the youngest of five.

"He ran away with her when she was twelve," Arthur's wife told us later, "and she had her first *chavie* before she was thirteen. If she had fed them for less time she'd have got two or three more."

The man was considered by many to be somewhat rough with her, and Arthur said that he had once nearly killed him with a tent rod for knocking the girl about when he was drunk. The children, however, looked exceptionally sturdy and bright, their bodies were dark and supple, their lips red, and their fine hair black and curly. The young mother did not look worn by the children she had borne and brought up; she appeared, on the other hand, to be thriving on her hardships. I looked at her sitting cross-legged by the fire; her face was full, dark, soft, her mouth was red, mobile, sensuous; her hair well kept in a rough fashion. When the baby awoke she sleepily pulled the clothes from her left shoulder and lifted the child to her breast. Although I could not conscientiously approve of the man making her have so many children in such a short space of time I found that I could not at the same time bring myself to justify the sacrifice of a single one of those five vivacious lives.

The fire died down, and when there was no wood left to replenish it the travellers one by one wished us good night and went to bed in their waggons or tents. The horses were untied from the hedge, led up the lane in pairs, and quietly slipped into an adjoining field. Normally they would have been hobbled or tethered in the lane, but as many of them were to be sold at the Fair it was thought inadvisable to take the risk of their getting caught up or kicked by our horse.

When the men returned we put a rope across the lane, let Sally loose, and crawled under the waggon, where we had previously made our beds. It was a fresh, clear night. I pulled the clothes over my shoulders and looked up at the stars which were visible through the spokes of the wheel. The candles had been extinguished in all the tents and waggons, and the lane was as quiet as it had been the previous night. The men and women and children sleeping in their camps seemed to strengthen the peace of the fields rather than destroy it.

The outline of a long-haired lurcher showed up under a cart. It turned round, scratched about in the sacks that had been thrown down for it to lie on, then curled up and slept. A breath of wind fanned the ashes of the fire, and sent minute bright sparks dancing over the top of the hedge and white ash fluttering about the lane.

❧ XIX ❧

When I awoke at daybreak no one was stirring in the camps, and in the half-light I could see our horse grazing some way up the lane. I wondered what had disturbed me, but before I could turn over and go to sleep again I heard the springs of the waggon in front creak. I watched indifferently and presently two bare feet descended the steps, and the half-clad figure of a girl appeared. I started and raised my head. For a moment I had thought that it was Britannia Ayres standing by the steps of the waggon, but as the girl approached, creeping beside the van, stopping to look up at the windows, I saw that her hair was a different colour and that she was not so old. It was her cousin, the daughter of Leander's sister. The discovery did not, however, completely relieve my state of mind, for as the girl drew nearer I saw that she had on very few clothes and that she was obviously under the impression that we were sleeping inside the waggon, the curtains of which were drawn.

English Gypsy girls in respect of their clothing are singularly modest. She held a torn blanket loosely round her dark, slim body, her brown shoulders were bare down to her full young breasts, her legs were bare, and in her hand she carried a small china cup.

I was aware of the embarrassment that would possess

her if she knew that I was lying awake under the waggon. In the environment of her people I had grown to understand her values and standard of modesty. I tried not to look at her, but my pulse beat singularly hard and I found that I could not do more than half close my eyes. Silently she crept up to the bucket which stood beside the shafts of our waggon, and after taking a last cautious look up at the windows she pushed her brown hair over her shoulders and knelt down. She dipped the cup into the water and lifted it to her lips. When she had drunk three cupfuls she looked satisfied, and rising to her feet returned to her waggon. I watched her bare feet ascending the steps and listened to it creaking as it tilted forward on the springs.

Between half-past five and six o'clock German Loveridge and the rough-looking man came up the lane and banged on the side of Arthur's tent. "*Awve avree* [come out]!" grunted the first, leaning against a cart-wheel and drawing at the end of a cigarette. There was a stir in the tent, and Arthur Loveridge, tying his handkerchief round his neck, stumbled out. The rough-looking man pushed a halter over Sally's head and tied her up to the hedge, then the three trudged up the lane and climbed over the end gate.

I dressed and collected a bundle of wood in the adjoining fields. The sun rose, but the sky was a deep red and I could see that the weather would not remain fine for long. When I returned to the camp the men were bringing the horses down the lane. The women came out of the waggons and tents, the fires smoked, the children got up and were sent up to the spring for water or to the fields to collect wood, and the men began grooming the horses ready for the Fair. In half an hour the quiet lane had been transformed into a tumult of activity—horses, breakfast, children getting up, washing, dressing, fires, smoke, shouting. It was Fair morning and every one was restless to be off. Every team of horses, decorated with blue ribbon and straw, that clattered up the hill, every cattle lorry that swept past the mouth of the lane, suggested that the Fair had begun and that it would be over before anyone left the lane.

I went to Arthur Loveridge's camp and offered to boil the kettle. The girl who had stolen our water at daybreak silently filled it while I asked her mother and father to bring their food to our camp and share our fire.

" I fancy there was a bit of a frost in the night," said Arthur as soon as we had started breakfast. " Didn't you find it cold lying under the waggon? "

" No," said Christopher, " we often sleep outside. I can stretch myself better than I can in the waggon."

As the man spoke I instinctively looked at the girl. Her eyes caught mine, and a sudden flash of mutual understanding passed between us. She was aware that I had been awake and she was aware of my impression. In turn I knew how she reacted to this disclosure. For an instant our eyes had been like two mirrors facing each other.

I turned quickly away, but it was too late; the eyes of the whole family were on her and she was blushing hotly. Looking to one side she tried to hide her face.

" What's the matter with you, girl! " shouted her mother. It was like the pounce of a tiger.

" Why are you hiding your face? " she continued, putting down her tea and leaning forward.

There was a stifling silence.

" Look up, girl! Look up, girl! What made the blood come to yer face then? You're hiding something very deep, child! "

Trapped, the girl turned and glared at her mother.

" I'm hiding nothing! " she shouted. " Would you take anyone's life away? " In desperation she buried her head in her hands.

" Tell me what you've done? " screamed the woman, brandishing a carving-knife over her head. " I'll beat the truth out of you if you don't speak! "

I leant forward and tapped the woman on the shoulder.

" I can tell you what is wrong with her," I said, half smiling. (A rebellious thought suddenly flitted through my mind—" Don't speak," it said; " you would like to see her to-morrow at daybreak.")

Every one turned to me, Christopher looked startled out of his life. The woman, ready to listen, half answered my smile, but I could see the hostility in her eyes.

" Your husband just now spoke about our sleeping under the waggon," I said. " Well, this morning, a little before daybreak your girl got up and fetched herself a drink. I was awake under the waggon, but the curtains were drawn and I think she was under the impression that we were asleep inside. I saw her look up at the windows before she went to our bucket, which was standing at the bottom of the steps. She only had a piece of a blanket round her, and when her father spoke she jumped to the conclusion that I had seen her."

The woman threw down the carving-knife and putting

her hands to her sides laughed just as her sister, Leander, always laughed. There is nothing that pleases a Gypsy more than 'straight-foridness.'

Arthur, Christopher, and the children also laughed, but the girl disappeared half under the hedge and sobbed until every one had left the fire.

At half-past eight two boys started off for the Fair with the horses which were to be sold by auction. Old Mr Loveridge came into the camp and, after talking for a few minutes, picked up our harness and carefully examined it.

"I tell you what, my son," he said at last, "I'll make a chop with you for this harness. I'll give you my chestnut colt."

"No," said Christopher, "we've made up our minds to keep our harness. We wouldn't let it go under any circumstances."

"I'll throw in a set of harness with the pony," persisted the old man. "Walk up to my place and look at the pony. I'll not force you to trade, my son."

We accompanied the old man to his camp, and when we had looked at the pony and harness he made a number of other suggestions—horses, waggons, money, traps, flat-carts, tents. At last he was forced to the conclusion that we really did not intend to make a deal; he shook us both by the hand and pulling off his silk handkerchief threw it on the ground.

"I cannot go to the Fair without trading with you, my boys," he said. "My mind will not rest content without I has a deal with one of you."

It was a good piece of silk with a Paisley pattern, and

I promptly took off mine and threw it on the ground. We then each picked up the other's handkerchief and shook hands.

When we returned to our camp we found German Loveridge intently examining the undercarriage of our waggon, and as soon as he became aware of our presence he instantly proposed making a chop for his van. Arthur, who had an eye on Sally, intervened and offered us thirty guineas for the horse. The rough-looking man said that it was in his mind to give us ten shillings for our old tent, and Noah, the girl's brother, was bent on exchanging his greyhound for Nell. We ended by selling the tent to the rough man for twelve and six.

At nine o'clock, when the dealing was over, the men returned to their camps and began to get ready for the Fair. Traps were pulled out into the lane and the driving horses brushed and harnessed. The children stood by the waggons—passive and suffering like the ponies while their rough hair was brushed or plaited, their faces washed and their handkerchiefs tied round their necks. Some of the girls helped their mothers dress the children and babies, others helped their fathers with the horses, and the rest went into the waggons, stood by the looking-glasses decorating their dark foreheads with arcs of flat, tight curls, and were called whores and mares for their vanity.

" *Dick* at the *lubni curring* her *bel*! [Look at the whore making up her hair!] " I heard an infuriated little girl, who could not plait her own hair, shout at her sister.

Christopher, who objected to leaving Sally unattended in the lane, took her to the public-house at the bottom of the hill and arranged to leave her in the paddock. I shut up the caravan, and when he returned the Gypsies were ready to start for the Fair. We climbed up into Arthur's trap and squeezed in between the children, who sat some on the floor and some on the tail-board with their feet dangling out over the road.

The rough-looking man and his wife and children turned out of the lane and started up the hill.

"Woman!" shouted Arthur, looking round for his wife, "I'm going."

"I don't mind if you goes and never returns," answered a voice from the tent. "I told you straight I was not a-going!" A cigarette between her lips, dressed in her rough-and-ready clothes, she came out into the open.

Arthur had had a dispute with her after breakfast, and she, sensitive and dramatic like her sister, had changed her clothes and made up her mind not to go to the Fair. The man sprang out of the trap and shaking his whip told her to get ready again.

"I'm not going to the Fair, and the Devil take you!" cried the woman.

Arthur returned to the trap and as we drove off he looked round and shouted, "If you don't come into the Fair this morning I'll knock the life out of you when I gets back!" He then cracked his whip and drove the pony as hard as he could down the lane and up the hill into the town.

In a few minutes we caught up with a four-wheel trap, which had joined the road at the top of the hill, packed with Gypsies, men and women and children. As we passed, the horses tearing along side by side, the travellers and their children shouted to one another, inquiring after relations and offering to deal in the same breath. On the outskirts of the town we drew up behind the traps of old Mr Loveridge, his son German, and the rough-looking man. The four-wheel trap was close behind, and as the noise of the five horses echoed through the streets the townspeople turned and stared with a look of hostile disapproval in their faces. It was inspired, I think, by the Oriental appearance of the Gypsies rather than by the unrestrained shouting and yelling of the children and the reckless way in which the men drove their horses along the slippery streets. The Eastern origin of the Gypsy is undoubtedly responsible for the greatest barrier between him and the European—a barrier which was strongly felt four or five centuries ago and still exists to-day.

We drove through the long, wide market-place and up the narrow main street to the Fair ground. It is a triangular piece of green beside the Marlborough road; the pleasure-fair occupies the first part and the horse-fair the end farthest from the town. Show-waggons and traction-engines stood by the railings on the edge of the green, and the road was full of horses going into the Fair, Gypsy women, children, and traps trotting to and fro. At the extreme end of the Fair ground a railing separates about one acre of the green, and it is here that the Gypsies tie up their horses. Several old women were sitting on the ground leaning against a trap and smoking their short clay pipes. Groups of men and women and children stood by the railings talking to relations whom they had not seen since the Autumn Fair, and watching the cattle and horses coming into the Fair ground. It is a great thing to be at a fair in time to see the horses arrive.

At eleven o'clock Arthur Loveridge took us down a narrow back-street to a public-house called the Carriage and Horses. The rooms were filled with Romany men and women, and the landlord and the barmen were the only house-dwellers I could see. It began to rain soon after we were inside, and one by one all the Gypsies left the Fair ground and pushed their way into the public-house until it was almost impossible to move and equally difficult to get served with beer.

In the bar my attention was attracted by a remarkable Romany standing in a corner by the window. He was a man of about thirty-five years, extremely good-looking, with features almost typically Indian and black hair so long that it hung round his shoulders. It was astonishing to see such long hair on a man and I pointed him out to Arthur and asked him his name.

"It is Oscar Deighton," answered our companion. "His hair is always like that."

"He has a fine-looking head," I remarked.

"Yes, he would have a fine-looking head on him, brother, if his nose was not crooked."

"If his nose was not crooked?"

"Look at him when he turns round."

I waited, and when he turned I saw that the line of his straight nose was slightly askew.

"How long has it been like that?" I asked, at the same time observing a scar on his face.

" It has only been crooked since his wife threw a teapot at him and broke it," replied Arthur drily.

" What made her do a thing like that? " said Christopher.

" Because she had no tobacco to smoke," Arthur said. " They were sitting by the fire having breakfast one morning. She is a savage-tempered young woman. She asked for some tobacco. Oscar said he'd got none, and she snatched up the teapot and threw it at him. I'd have beat the life out of her if I'd been him. But, God strike me blind, Oscar would let her kill him afore he'd lay his fist on her ! "

" Is he afraid of her? "

" I couldn't tell you that, young man, but I can tell you that there is many good fighting men who wouldn't stand up to one round with him," replied Arthur. " He can fight like a kicking horse."

" And did he do nothing when she threw the teapot at him? "

" Not a thing, young man."

" Was the woman upset when she discovered what she'd done? "

" She was so bloody angry that she cut up the harness and smashed up all the crocks. She'd be a lot better if he'd thrash her every now and then."

A gaunt-looking man with a hollow face and an immense gold watch-chain across his waistcoat pushed his way into the middle of the room and called for order.

" Order, please ! Order ! " he called above the shouting and talking.

A brief silence was at last secured, and German Loveridge took off his hat and began singing.

" Oh a wager, a wager, I wouldn't mind betting you,
  I'll bet you twenty guineas to your one
  That you don't ride a maid to the bonny green bush bloom——"

Two women began fighting in one corner of the room
and a pint mug fell with a crash to the ground.

" Order, please ! "

" And a maiden she shall return back again."

In the commotion which followed the breaking of the
glass I missed several verses. When I again picked up the
thread of the song I gathered that an allusion had been
made to the evil influences of the " bonny green bush
bloom " and that a narrative had begun.

" Three times he did walk to the bottom of her feet,
  Three times to the crown of her head,
  Three times he did kiss her red rosy cheeks
  As she lay on the ground dead."

" Order, please ! "

" He took the ring from his middle finger
  And placed it in his true love's right hand
  To let them know that her true love had been there,
  That her true love had killed her and gone."

" Order, please ! "

" Why hadn't you awoken me, my faithful greyhound dog,
  Why hadn't you awoken me before?
  For you I would have killed and your blood I would have
      spilled
  And left the small birds in the wood to have their fill.

  Oh, you I would have killed, your blood I would have spilled
  And left the small birds in the wood to have their fill."

When German Loveridge had finished a young Gypsy whom I did not know took off his cap and began another song. The gaunt man now found it necessary to shout "Order, please!" between every line, instead of between every verse, and I was only able to catch a few words of the song.

> " I like you true and holy for what you have done,
> For taking of your own part and firing of your gun.
> You come with me, my fair pretty maid,
> You come with me this way.
> I'll take you a nearer cut across the country."

I have never been able to perfect the words of this song, but the fact that these old ballads are sung to-day, not as relics of antiquity but in the same spirit with which they were written, is to me interesting in itself.

Presently, above the shouting and singing, I heard the rattle of a step-dance. Two men were producing a horn-pipe rhythm with their mouths, and old Mr Loveridge, holding a pint mug in his hand, was dancing. I asked Art'ur why there was no music, and he explained that usually there were several travellers with mouth-organs and melodeons at the Fair, but that so far none had arrived.

" Can you play a mouth-organ? " Christopher asked.

" Yes, have you got one? "

" No, but I can very soon get one."

We sent a small Gypsy boy into the town with a two-shilling piece, and when he returned we gave the instrument to Arthur. He played several bars of a lively horn-pipe, but the dancer found it impossible to hear. Either the commotion had increased while the boy was away or the humming had been louder than the mouth-organ.

"Give it to me!" cried the gaunt Gypsy impatiently. "You'll do nothing with it like that."

Taking the instrument from Arthur he poured half my beer through the reeds, and when he began playing I was astonished at the difference in volume. We formed a circle and the gaunt Gypsy literally blew into the dancer's ears.

Between half-past twelve and one o'clock I found that the beer was beginning to make my head swim, and I walked up to the Fair ground and watched the horses being sold in the auction. Presently I explored the pleasure-ground and after wandering among the side-shows and roundabouts met the boy Noah, who explained that he was a very skilful hand at the coconut-shies and persuaded me to speculate with sixpence. His first attempts only succeeded in knocking a nut to one side, but after he had expressed profound surprise at his temporary lack of skill and promised to give his coconuts, should he win any, to his sister, I gave him another sixpence.

"Do you think your mother and Miranda will come into the Fair this afternoon?" I asked while the boy threw the balls.

"Not unless some one goes back after them. Why don't you drive the pony and fetch 'em? I'll go with you."

"I cannot do that. Your father might want to make a chop for the pony," I said. "Let's see if we can win a packet of cigarettes on the rifle-range."

We moved on to the next stall.

"Watch me put it straight in the bull's eye, brother,"

said the boy when I had paid the showman. Crack!
" Father would never see that the pony was gone."

" How old is your sister? "

Crack! " Fifteen and a half."

" She looks older."

" Yes. It's funny how they fill out all of a sudden. One
day their clothes hang on 'em, and the next day they seems
to be a-bursting out of 'em."

I succeeded in winning a packet of cigarettes. I left the
boy deeply engrossed in the erection of the " wall of death "
and walked back to the horse auction. Presently I saw a
friend among the crowd. I pushed my way in between
the dealers and farmers and when I reached him we walked
to one side and talked. He was a relation of a celebrated
writer, and his interest in vagrant life had brought him to
the Devizes Fair. He was, however, one of those obstinate
inquirers who have a firm conviction that the only remaining Gypsies live in the mountains and towns of the romantic
Balkans. With a wave of his hand in the direction of one
or two *diddikies* [half-caste Gypsies] he complained that
there was not a true Gypsy in the whole Fair. It was a
subject on which we had argued on several former occasions.

" What time did you get here? " I asked.

" About half-past eleven or twelve," he replied.

" And what time are you leaving? Will you be here at
four o'clock? "

" No, I'm catching a bus at three-thirty. You seem to
attach a great deal of importance to the time that I arrived
and the time when I intend to leave."

" I do," I replied, " and if you were not so respectably

dressed I would offer to take you to a small, unassuming public-house, in a back-street behind the Fair ground, where at present all the true Gypsy men and women in this Fair are making themselves drunk."

"I don't think you would be able to convince me," said the *gorgio*.

"Nor do I," I said. "To make an impression on you I would have to replace their mouth-organs with violins, their pints of beer and stout with exotic wines, and their stitched corduroys with the picturesque clothes of Rumanian peasants." At half-past three I saw this same inquirer depart on a district bus.

When I returned to the Carriage and Horses two women were dancing an Irish jig together. The gaunt Gypsy perspired more and more as he played and during the next dance, in his effort to meet with the increasing noise and brawl, he blew out the guts of our two-shilling mouth-organ. Fortunately within the next quarter of an hour a man with an excellent four-reed German melodeon arrived, and the dancing began again with redoubled energy.

At four o'clock, when the public-house was due to close, the interest in the step-dancing was so great that it could not be stopped. The men argued excitedly as to which was the best dancer, and crowded round the circle in the middle of the floor as if it held a pair of fighting-cocks. An enraged father forced his daughter to dance again and again in an attempt to prove that she was the best dancer at the Fair. Another man insisted that his brother was the best, another swore that he was himself champion, the onlookers shouted their own opinions, while the unfortunate dancers were snatched on and off the floor so quickly that it was impossible for anyone to reach a fair decision. Arthur Loveridge watched with amusement and repeatedly told them that in the evening he would bring in a traveller who would, the Devil take his breath, dance every other Gypsy in the Fair off his feet! He was a stranger, and Arthur's report that he could step-dance on four pennies without moving any one of them did not fail to make an impression.

The landlord, exasperated and hoarse, repeatedly called time. Still the melodeon thumped out the quick jerking rhythm and the men and women continued to sing and dance and call for more beer. At a quarter-past four he pushed his way into the bar and attempted to stop the dancing by force, but his efforts were only met by a cry of " One more step! One more step, Mr Landlord! " So long as the music continued no one attempted to move, and in final desperation the man bolted out of the door and disappeared in the direction of the police-station.

The dancing and singing went on and the clock pointed to half-past four. Then a shout echoed down the passage, and the Superintendent, followed by six constables, pushed his way into the crowded building. In a few minutes the passage and the two bars were cleared and the travellers flocked into the street. At closing-time on Fair days a crowd always collects outside in the hope of seeing a fight among the Gypsies, and on this occasion the arrival of the police attracted an extra number of people.

The travellers stood in groups, talking, quarrelling, and singing, the police locked the doors and stood outside waiting to subdue any disturbances. Five or ten minutes elapsed and no one attempted to move up to the Fair ground; the drunken ones ceased to sing, the quarrelling ones ceased to wrangle, and a group of men and women in the middle of the road whispered uneasily together. I asked Arthur what was wrong, but he had only just finished an argument with his sister and was equally anxious to discover the cause of the suspense. Presently a young Gypsy driving a horse and waggonette trotted down the road from the Fair ground. Outside the public-house he stopped, jumped to the ground, and with an agitated look approached the Superintendent. A flicker of a smile passed over the latter's face and then after a brief discussion—the one grave, the other earnest—he motioned to the constables at the door. A similar smile lightened their faces, the door was opened, and the young man, followed by two of the crowd, entered the building.

After a tense interval the door was reopened, the rack of the waggonette was lowered, and the Gypsy, assisted by the two men, struggled down the passage with his father, who had been left under a table in the public-house. The unconscious man was hoisted up into the back of the cart and driven up to the Fair ground, where he remained until nightfall.

☙ XX ☙

IT IS DURING THE BRIEF INTERVAL WHEN THE PUBLIC-HOUSE is closed that the Gypsies conduct the greater part of their business. On the road which runs beside the Fair ground the men brought out their horses and trotted them furiously up and down. Recklessly they manœuvred their traps through the crowd. Wheels were held, arms nearly wrenched off, while half-broken colts plunged, reared, kicked, backed and bit. The road was a confusion of frightened colts, children, and excited men and women.

The men who were out for trade stood in the middle of the road watching the action of horses and examining their mouths, legs, feet, and shoulders. At intervals, before these prospective dealers, a driver would bring his animal to a sudden standstill, its back legs sliding under it so that its haunches almost touched the ground. Springing out of the trap he would seize a wheel, crack his long whip, and send the horse plunging wildly into the collar.

For some time I had been watching a small, active man driving a beautiful fiery chestnut up and down the road. The ears of the animal were thrown back, its head tossed, and the foam from its mouth was blown back on the trap and the driver. At every turn up and down the road it grew more vicious and the man more excited and anxious to prove that he possessed the finest horse in the Fair. Presently he jerked the horse to a standstill, pulling himself upright on the reins, and shouted for some one to hold the wheels.

" Hold that wheel, my brothers ! " he cried to a group of men beside the trap. " Hold that wheel and I'll show you whether she's collar-proud or not ! "

The men, who were at that moment occupied with another deal, were not quick enough.

" Hold that bastard wheel ! " he yelled again, then throwing down the reins he sprang out of the trap.

As he seized the spokes of the wheel the horse reared into the breeching and sent the trap flying backwards. In a second the man was flung on the ground with his arm thrust in between the spokes. Before he could recover himself the horse plunged forward, twisting his arm between the springs and the spokes of the wheel, and dragging him along the road half under the trap. When he was lifted to his feet his arm was bleeding profusely and, as we afterwards discovered, the bone was badly fractured. It was with great difficulty that he was persuaded to get into another trap and go to the hospital to have it dressed. He finally went on the strict understanding that he was not left there. The police cleared the road and when the various deals had been completed the travellers dispersed.

In the Fair I met Noah, who said that his father wanted me to drive the pony back to the lane and fetch his wife and daughter. I was a little suspicious.

" I was with him ten minutes ago," I said, " and he said nothing to me about it."

" Oh, he makes up his mind very quickly," replied the boy. " You see, mè mother's got all the *vongar* [money], and he's got none for himself. If she don't come he'll chop away the pony and draw some money."

"Well, I'd better go and see him first."

"I shouldn't if I were you, brother. You see, he changes his mind as quickly as he makes it up. We'll be back in less than half an hour if we get off now."

"Do you think your mother will come back, Noah?"

"I shouldn't think so."

"Then what's the good of going?"

"Miranda will come back with us. She was miserable, brother, 'cos she didn't come to the Fair this morning, and no doubt she'll let me have enough money to buy you a drink. It don't seem right to leave the poor girl there all day—speak the truth!—does it?"

"No, but I think I'll speak to your father before we start."

"Very well," said the boy. "You can say that you want to fetch something out of yer waggon while you'm there— that's just in case his mind's changed. There he is, with your brother!"

We pushed our way through the crowd and caught up with Arthur Loveridge.

"Dad!" shouted Noah. "The young man said that he would drive back to the place. He wants to fetch some *covels* [things] out of his waggon. Shall we take the pony and bring Mother back, the same as I said?"

The man evidently knew his son's artful ways too well to be surprised at the sudden adoption of a casual suggestion made by him and forgotten two hours ago.

"You can take the pony back if the young man will go

with you," he said. "Tell yer mother that I sent back for her. If she won't come, tell her to send some money, a pound or twenty-five shillings. No, let the young man ask for it. You say that I want her, young man, and drive the pony yerself—the boy will throw him down before you're out of the town."

"Hurry up!" urged the boy, pushing between the people who were crowded round the stalls. "Let's get off quick afore he changes his mind and goes and chops the pony away or summat—push on!"

He untied the pony and backed the trap out into the green. I took the reins and we trotted quickly out of the Fair ground and through the town. When we reached the lane we found the woman sitting by the fire in a rough-and-ready *lue* which she had erected in front of the tent. Miranda and the youngest child were coming across the fields with bundles of wood on their backs. I lit a cigarette with a firebrand and gave the woman her husband's message.

"No, I'm in the same mind as I was this morning," she replied. "It's no good for him to send after me—I told him I should not go to the fair."

The girl crawled through the hedge and came into the tent.

"Miranda," said the woman, turning to her daughter, "you can go back with them if you want to."

The girl did not answer. I did my best to persuade the woman to come, but when I saw that nothing would change her mind I mentioned the money for which her husband had asked.

"Ah! I thought he wouldn't send a horse and trap back for his woman," she cried.

She loaded us with a heavy burden of abuse to take back to her husband, but stoutly declined to send back a shilling.

"A sovereign! A sovereign or twenty-five shillings!" she exclaimed. "Has the man gone right out of his mind? Does he think I'm a-going to send him twenty-five shillings to make himself staggering, blind drunk?"

"If you don't send it him, woman," cried Noah, "he'll chop Prince away, draw money, and get more bloody blind drunk than he'd ever get on twenty-five shillings!"

"Chop away Prince! If he dares to get rid of my pony I'll kill him stone dead to-night!" The woman jumped up from the fire. "You'll leave that pony here! Get out and unharness it, girl!"

The girl did not move.

"You knows what he'd do to you if you keeps the pony here!" said the boy. "You'd be lying dead to-morrow and he'd be swinging from a gibbet. Send him the money if you don't want him to come back to-night and beat the place down."

"I shall not send him a penny, boy!"

Noah managed to *mong* [beg] two shillings for himself, after which we returned to the trap. I turned the pony round and waited to see if the girl were coming.

"Jump up and push ahead!" the boy said impatiently.

"I am going to wait for your sister," I replied firmly. No one moved in the tent, and presently I went back and looked inside. "Miranda," I said, "I'm waiting for you."

"Can I go, Mother?" asked the girl.

" Yes, you can go so long as you see that yer father don't sell the pony."

The girl rose and in silence fetched a rough black coat from the caravan and climbed up in the trap. The traffic on the road had begun to light up, but by driving the pony fast we managed to get through the town before dark. As I turned into the Fair ground I heard shouting and in the twilight I could see a crowd of men and women gathered round two young men who were preparing to fight. I drove the pony up to the railing and after we had tied it up we joined the crowd. It was two Gypsy brothers who I was told had quarrelled in the public-house in the morning. The youngest, whose lip had been split open, had appeared frightened of his brother, but after closing-time he had waited on the green and had now torn off his coat, shirt, shoes and stockings with the intention of settling the dispute. At first the elder brother was reluctant to accept the challenge, but soon he too pulled off his jacket and shirt and put up his fists.

In the true Gypsy style they both held their arms close to their sides so as to protect their ribs, and fought hard and fast. In a few moments each had scored several terrific hits. The hard bleeding fist of the elder brother landed with a thud on the other's swollen split lip. The next blow felled him to the ground, but when the latter sprang to his feet he fought with greater spirit, and within a few minutes his opponent was sprawled on the grass with his left eye closed and his mouth also bleeding.

When the excitement caused by the victory of the younger brother was over, we walked down to the Carriage

and Horses. Arthur Loveridge accepted his wife's message
with sullen fury, but was somewhat softened by the presence
of his daughter, of whom he appeared to be extremely fond.
He gave her a glass of beer, after which I took her up to the
pleasure-fair, where we found Christopher and her cousins
spinning round in the chair-a-planes. I shouted out to them,
then taking Miranda's arm I boarded one of the modernized
merry-go-rounds. We then explored all the side-shows.
The boxing booth pleased her, the headless woman disgusted her, the bearded woman annoyed her, the smallest
pony and the biggest dog delighted her, the " wall of death "
and the lions frightened her.

We climbed up into one of the deserted swinging-boats
which stood on the outskirts of the pleasure-fair. I started
the boat swinging and lit a cigarette.

" Can I have one? " said the girl.

" Yes, I didn't know you smoked."

" I don't, except when I is alone."

" You aren't alone now."

" I know, but I'se not going to smoke it now. Look!
There's your brother and my cousins on the roundabouts.
Let's go back, they'll wonder where I've got to."

" Not yet."

" Isn't it quiet up here, after being agen those noisy
organs."

I looked down at the throngs of people and the brilliant
lights.

" Why don't you light your cigarette now? "

" No."

" Why? "

" Because I feel dizzy."

" The effect of the beer or the swinging-boats? "

" I think—I think it's both of them. I must go back to the *livno-ker* [public-house]. If me father sells the pony I'll get *marred* [beaten or killed]. Come on, please."

" I like to watch your hair fly out behind you when we go down."

" Well, you mustn't. What does that clock on the tower above that stall say? "

" Quarter to nine. Can't you tell the time? "

" No, but I can keep count of the time in the day."

" Did you ever go to school? "

" Oh, yes, the teacher said that if I had stayed longer she could have taught me to read and write."

" How long did you stay? "

" Nearly six weeks. The only thing that used to worry them was that I used to write from the right-hand side of the paper to the left. I should like to be a good scholar like yourself."

" When I look into those dark eyes of yours I feel that you know far more than I do. I wonder if you would know so much if you were a good scholar."

" I expect I should, but I'm not quite sure whether I wants to be a scholar. Stop it now, or I'll be sick."

We climbed down and I pushed my way behind the engines and waggons with the intention of making a short cut back to the public-house.

" Come on, Miranda," I said, waiting for the girl to follow.

" Let's go through the Fair."

" No, it's quicker this way. Don't you like the smell of the hot steam? "

" I is not going all round there in the dark."

" Why, can't you trust yourself with me? "

" No—yes—well, I'm not going to."

" Come on, I shall feel miserable if you won't trust me."

" You wouldn't."

" I would."

" What do you think I shall do to you in the dark? "

" I don't know. I don't know you, and I wouldn't go into the dark with you if I did."

" Is there anyone you would go into the dark with? "

" No. I want to get back."

" Will you another time? "

" I might."

" When? "

" Next Fair, if you'll come on now."

When we returned to the Carriage and Horses we found Arthur in the passage in the middle of chopping away his pony with another traveller. He was half drunk, but alive to the situation and arguing for a draw of two pounds. The girl, despite her instructions, did not attempt to interfere, for she knew that when her father had made up his mind to do anything no one could stop him, unless it was his wife. Miserably she watched the deal progress and the money paid over.

The public-house was more crowded and riotous than ever, but from the bar step-dancing and the sound of the melodeon was still audible. Christopher and German Loveridge came into the passage, and Arthur having

ROMANY GIRL

ordered drinks for us all took us into the bar to meet the
stranger who step-danced on four pennies. He was a slen-
der, agile man, sixty or sixty-five years of age, and after a
little persuasion from Arthur and the gaunt man an exceptionally large space of the floor was cleared, the four coins
adjusted, and the remarkable feat performed. The pennies
were moved very little by the dancing, and every step
struck a clear, metallic note on the surface of a coin.

The man continued to demonstrate various other feats
of dancing until every one's attention was distracted by a
great uproar which suddenly broke out by the window.
Two girls had started fighting and pints of beer and bottles
were sent spinning onto the floor. The enraged girls did
not scratch or tear each other's hair, but with whirling fists
struck their opponent right and left on the face and body.
Blood gushed from one's mouth, and before anyone could
effectively separate them there was a shattering of glass and
the other crashed through the window. Everything became
covered with blood, and as if from nowhere the police
pushed their way into the bar. The girl, fortunately, was
not very badly cut, but by the time she had been bandaged
up and the commotion had died down it was ten o'clock.
The police cleared the public-house, and laden with bottles
the travellers streamed out into the road.

On reaching the green we were told that the rough-
looking man had fallen off the roundabouts and broken
both his legs. German Loveridge drove his pony to the
scene of the accident and brought back the man, screwed
up in agony, in the bottom of the cart. The extent of the
injury had been greatly exaggerated, for he had only twisted

his knee and his ankle, and when he had recovered sufficiently we got him into his own trap and helped his wife light the lamps and harness the pony.

Arthur took the harness off Prince and buckled it on the new pony which he had taken in exchange. The boy kicked up a great fuss when he discovered what had taken place and swore at his sister for allowing the exchange; she in return reproached him for going away and not looking after the pony. It was, however, an extremely good-looking roan, and until we were out of the town I was surprised that Arthur had succeeded in drawing two pounds on the deal. Several travellers drove away with only one off-side light on their traps. We were the last to leave the Fair ground and when Arthur was ready to start I discovered that he had no lamps at all. German Loveridge and the old man with the side-whiskers were some way on in front and there was nothing we could do but drive back as quickly as we could without lights. We turned down a side-street and made our way round the middle of the town without encountering a policeman. The pony trotted briskly along and Arthur seemed pleased enough with the exchange, but the girl appeared to be almost terrified and kept her eyes on the animal's head as if she expected it to bolt, or shy, or fall at any moment.

" Drive her steady, Dad ! " she cried at last. " I don't like the pony. As soon as I saw it on the green I didn't like it."

" Keep quiet ! " said her father. " The pony's got some life in it. I'll give you something to be frightened about if you don't sit back and keep quiet."

With that he jerked the rein and the pony tore on faster and faster through the dimly lit streets. Out on the main road beyond the market-place we just managed to avoid running down a policeman who was standing in the shadow of the houses. He shouted, but Arthur continued to drive at the same speed until we came to the first hill which runs down from Devizes. It was then that the trouble arose which Miranda had already anticipated. Her father began to pull up, and as the breeching tightened the pony's ears went back, its legs slid under it, and the trap came to a standstill.

" Get on, little mare ! " said Arthur, softly at first. " Get on, little mare ! "

He jerked the rein, but the pony remained stock-still, its haunches tight into the breeching.

" Get on, you stubborn mare ! " he shouted, lashing out with his whip. " I'll show you who is master ! Get on ! "

The pony viciously ran the trap back against the bank and began kicking. Arthur sprang up and beat the horse with his whip, but the iron shoes continued to smash against the floor and splashboard, splintering the wood in all directions. The children clambered out at the back and I, under Arthur's directions, grabbed the pony's head and quickly pulled her round so that she was obliged to keep her hoofs on the ground. I then ran forward until she was almost in a trot.

The children clambered in behind and I jumped up again beside Christopher, and when we reached a flat stretch of road at the bottom of the hill the pony began kicking again, but Arthur was ready with the whip and a lash across its back sent it flying on to the next hill. Here it started backing and kicking for nearly ten minutes. When we swung into the lane the other travellers were unharnessing their horses in the light of their newly kindled fires. Arthur's wife was standing outside her tent.

"This is a bloody fine time to come back to your wife and child," she shouted as we approached. Then, as she caught sight of the strange pony and broken splashboard, the storm which had been gathering all day broke. She swore at him for having sold the pony and he swore at her for not having come to the Fair and for not having sent the money. Her anger, however, appeared to be a compensation for the bad deal he had made. A Romany generally does not care how much money a row with his wife or a day at a Fair costs him.

The other travellers on their arrival in the lane had warned Georgina that her husband was in a savage temper and that he had threatened to beat her. Arthur jumped out of the trap and while he and the woman shouted at each other we took the pony out and poured out some beer. Georgina seemed at first a little frightened of being knocked about, but gradually she worked herself up into a frenzy until I thought they would both kill each other. When we had tied the pony up we went along to German Loveridge's camp, where the old Mr Loveridge and the rough-looking man had collected round the fire drinking. It was a warm, starry night and while the row went on in Arthur's camp the fire crackled, sending up showers of sparks into the sky.

At about half-past twelve the boy and girl came up to

the fire and, after telling us not to take any notice of the row between their father and mother, wished us good night and went to bed. Arthur himself presently joined the circle and drank a mugful of beer. There was a dreamy chorus of singing, and when at about two o'clock in the morning I grew so tired that I could no longer keep my eyes open I climbed into the waggon and dreamt that I was living, with surprising contentment, in a swinging-boat with Arthur's dark, pretty, and untidy girl.

After I had slept for about three hours I was awakened suddenly. It was some time before I realized where I was, but as soon as my mind cleared I discovered that it was Arthur's and Georgina's voices that had disturbed me. I listened intently, but though their tent was quite close I could not understand what they were saying. Presently I became drowsy and turning over I tried to get to sleep again. A half-hour must have elapsed, and then gradually their voices grew louder and louder until to hear it was no longer necessary to listen.

It was Georgina's voice that first became strident.

"Don't talk to me about your brother, dog's face—or I'll go and find him this very day and tell just what I think on 'en and his whole clan. You're a bad breed, all of you! Drown every Loveridge at birth, I would, if I had my way. A blasted sight better, too—"

Arthur's voice broke in.

"Shut yer foul mouth up, woman, or I'll break your head open with my fist—"

"You'll do what? You couldn't break a matchbox with both yer fists put together."

" You great *lubni* [whore]—go to sleep. I'll get up and beat you if you don't ! "

" Call me a *lubni*, will you, you b——? You'll beat me? I'll poke your eyes out, man ! "

" The Devil take you ! You come from a lousy, poxy breed ! "

" You dirty Loveridge, don't you dare say a word against my dead father and mother what's gone ! "

" I didn't speak about your father and mother. I said the lot of you—every Hearne that ever breathed ! "

" I disgraced them by going with such a man as you ! "

" Why did you come with me, then? I never wanted you nor all your brats."

" It was a different story before you had me—what about the time you lay all night on the cold ground outside my tent and caught pneumonia? "

" I never did anything of the sort, you lying, blasphemous woman ! "

" You ought to have had your cousin 'Lisa ! Pretty little dear ! You'd have just suited her ! "

" She'd 'ave made a better woman than you ! "

" Well, go and 'ave 'er, the little whore ! Go and 'ave 'er—go and sleep with 'er—lie with 'er—give her some of yer wretched brats and see how she likes them ! You won't never sleep with me again, I tell you that, man ! "

" You'll never get the chance. I'll pack up and get out of it ! "

" Yes ! Go to yer 'Lisa, and I hope she'll break yer face in with the kettle iron—she won't, though, 'cos she ain't got the sense. Pretty dear, I wish her luck."

"I'd be better off with her than I ever was with you, woman!"

"Then get up and go to her now, dog's face! Go to her now, I say! You bastard! Get out of my sight!"

By this time I began to get alarmed. Georgina was screaming and shouting with all her might, and Arthur was roaring back at her with almost—but not quite—equal fury. The last raging of Georgina was accompanied by a great noise and clatter from within the tent.

"Stop throwing the things about!" roared Arthur. "You'll kill your own child in a minute. Get back in bed and lie down, or by God I'll get up and thrash you to death! Stop throwing the things about, I tell you!"

Their voices became quite unintelligible. It was still quite dark, but just as I was reflecting that it would be unwise to interfere and that I had better pull the clothes over my head and try to get to sleep a great flare of light shone in through the door of the waggon. This was followed by a crackling and a hissing, and jumping up I looked out and saw that Arthur's tent was in flames. I was determined not to interfere so I remained where I was and watched. Arthur, stark naked, soon appeared through the flames and began wrestling with the fire. He tore the canvas off the framework, threw water on it, and beat the flames out with a board. Georgina's anger didn't seem to abate in the least, and all the time that Arthur was occupied with the fire she cursed him violently. At last every spark was extinguished, and flinging down the board he caught Georgina roughly by the arm and dealt her such a blow on the face that I thought she would be stunned. But no, as soon as she had recovered she retaliated, striking him right and left with astonishing rapidity. Arthur stood it for a moment, then as quick as lightning dealt her two smashing blows; she fell on the grass, where she remained while Arthur went to the remains of the tent and commenced dressing.

The sun was shining and the birds were singing when I next woke, but remembering the ructions of the night I listened carefully for any echoes which might suggest that the storm had not yet abated. Except for the murmur of the children, who were now abroad, there was a peaceful silence. " Ah," I said to myself, " all is well," but, just as I was about to compliment myself upon not interfering, Georgina's voice cut through the atmosphere.

" Leave the food alone, man, or I'll break all the crocks over your head."

" You'll have to eat out of your dirty hands if you do."

I shook Christopher and we dressed and went up to our neighbour's fire. Arthur and Georgina and the children all wished us good morning.

" *Kooshto suti, pral?* [Good sleep, brother?] " said the man.

" *Awal* [yes]."

" I should have slept well myself if it hadn't been for that blasphemous man lying beside me," said Georgina.

" Don't take any notice of that woman, young man ! Sit down by the fire while I go for a drop of water. That cow of a woman went and set the tent alight in the night and I had to use up all the water putting it out. I don't like a woman, brother, who'd set a tent alight with her own child inside."

" Do you never stop talking, man? I'd give all "—she waved her hand expressively—" the money in the world to be away from that man. Strike me dead, I would! "

" I'll push you in the fire, woman, if you keep on," said Arthur, coming back and glaring at her. " I'll push you in the fire if I have any more of your *chib* [tongue]."

" Go on and get out of my sight! "

When Arthur had disappeared up the lane she turned to us. " I hope none of my girls gets hold of a man like he," she remarked confidentially. Miranda, who always sat by the fire with her legs crossed, looked at her mother and smiled. She was invariably preoccupied if she was not hungrily watching for food.

When Arthur returned we fetched our cooking utensils and prepared breakfast. Throughout the meal the man and woman quarrelled continuously, and all our attempts to make peace were in vain. The young children were far too occupied in filling their hungry mouths to be in the least perturbed by the dispute. Occasionally with a confidential nod they hinted that the quarrel was nothing very unusual and was to be taken quite as a matter of course. Frequently they shrieked with laughter at an expression used by their father or mother, but scarcely for a minute did their hungry eyes leave the food hamper over which Georgina presided. Among Gypsies there are few conventions respecting greed. A healthy person has necessarily a hungry belly; whether there is enough to fill it is a matter of circumstances.

After breakfast Georgina took a knife and cut up the harness. This is a common occupation of Gypsy women

when they have a row with their husbands; but it is, however, generally regarded as a crisis of a family upheaval.
The man usually beats his wife, or repairs the harness with
rope and string, hitches the pony in the trap, and leaves
his *juvel* [wife] for two or three days. In this instance
Arthur, who valued his harness, chose the first method of
retaliation. I would not, however, go as far as to say that
the value of the harness has always a bearing on the decision.
The unfortunate Georgina was knocked about and afterwards thrown into the hedge, where she lay sobbing and
with an occasional volley of curses condemning her husband's soul to eternal hell.

The Gypsy man, like the Gypsy woman, has his tradi-
tional methods of revenge. The woman cuts up the harness,
rips the tent and bedding, and breaks the crockery; the
man smashes up the trap with the kettle iron, sells the
pony for half its worth, and does as much damage as he
can about the camping-place in order to annoy the neighbouring farmers. The police arrive and order him to move,
the harness is lying cut up on the grass, the tent is ripped
to pieces, the trap is smashed, and the horse is sold. He
then feels he has sufficiently annoyed his wife. Fortunately
Arthur was content with having picked up the 'bouncer'
(kicking horse) at the Fair.

❧ XXI ❧

AT HALF-PAST TEN WE HEARD HORSES COMING DOWN THE hill, and presently two Romany men whom we had seen at the Fair swung into the lane. One was driving a pony and trap and the other a cob and four-wheeled dog-cart.

"Here come the Fair men out for trade," said old Mr Loveridge, who was standing in the lane talking to us.

The Gypsy driving the four-wheeled trap pulled up in Arthur's camp while the other stopped at the mouth of the lane.

"Let's hear what they've got to say," said the old man.

We followed him into the camp, where the newcomer, after talking by the fire for ten minutes, began dealing with Arthur.

"You picked up a bouncer at the Fair," he said, "but I knows just where to place her. The pony's a good driver, but it's no good to you, my brother. God strike me down if I tell you a lie! I knows that pony! It's no good to a man that's travelling on the roads, it's no good to a man that's got little children! I've got no little children, Arthur. I am not afraid of any horse that's living, but I wouldn't keep that animal, God take my breath, a day longer than I could help it! I'll give you as good a deal as you will get from any travelling man in this country."

Arthur got up and examined the newcomer's horse. It was a young horse and a fine-looking animal.

"You could trust yer life with that horse," went on the newcomer. "You could let a baby crawl up its legs." To demonstrate he bent down and crawled under the animal's belly. "Jump up, Arthur, and I'll drive you into the town. I want you to see that I offer you a fair and straightforward deal." He swung the pony round again and climbed up. "Get up too, my brothers, if you have a mind to," he said, addressing us.

We sprang into the trap, and German Loveridge, who appeared to be dying for the want of a drink, joined us, his wife following down the lane shouting and daring him to go into a public-house. We stopped at the Carriage and Horses, where quite a number of travellers were dealing together. We drank several pints of beer, and while Arthur and the newcomer argued over their deal Christopher discovered that he had no money left. I told him that I had nothing and we were suddenly faced with the fact that we had not sufficient to buy food for our supper and breakfast.

"We shall have to get off early to-morrow morning," he said, "and find a means of making some money. We've got a good horse and a comfortable waggon, but we must have something to eat. When we left Elias we arranged to go to Yorkshire, so let us start away in the morning. If we travel every day and camp at night in lanes and on the roadside the horse will cost us nothing and it will be easier to make money and if necessary beg food when we are on the move. I should like to travel in a strange part of the country and camp in a different place every night."

When we returned to the lane Arthur Loveridge exchanged his waggon and new pony for the cob, the trap, and four pounds of the stranger's money. The rough man also sold his waggon, and in the late afternoon we found ourselves in a near-by coppice helping the two men cut hazel sticks for the tents in which they would live during the spring and summer. A multitude of warm sunny days when the grass would be long and the trees green were before them; and while they wandered from lane to lane camping in the shade of hedges and trees they would not think about waggons and *lues* until the Devizes Fall Fair at the end of October.

On our return to the camp we sat round the fire with Arthur and his wife and children. We had not mentioned the position in which we had suddenly found ourselves, and we were both taken aback when Arthur, without a word to us, abruptly told his wife to give us an equal share of the tea which had been cooking on the fire. Arthur was silent while we ate and then, with equal suddenness, made a direct allusion to the circumstances which we had only realized ourselves five hours before. At first we attempted to conceal the truth, but Arthur persisted and we ended by giving him an exact account of our position. Like Ira Lovell he was deeply concerned about our future and immediately asked us to travel with him.

" I have got a two-pound hawking licence on my cart," he said. " If the three of us stick together, brother, we can do ourselves a bit of good. You've got yerselves a flash turn-out. You've got the prettiest waggon, horse, and harness I've seen for ten years. Young man, you want to hang on to that turn-out like you'd hang on to your dear life. Jesus Christ, may He strike me stone blind, I'm telling you the truth! There are both travellers and house-dwellers who will spill their own blood to take that away from you. *Mong, buti* [beg, work], but don't sell your waggon or your horse or your harness."

He kicked the fire and threw out the piece of smoking wood.

"If you see a cheap horse and you want to buy it I shan't be a-feared of lending you money. Travelling about the country together we can do plenty of dealing. You can eat with us, the girl can wash your clothes, and I'll take an oath that if you do as I tell you you will have a hundred sovereigns in the bank by next Fall Fair."

I was conscious of two strong impulses tearing me in two different directions. The first was wild and natural the second practical and depressing. The first was an end in itself, the second a means to an end. To live. To begin writing. Christopher insisted upon the necessity of starting our move to Yorkshire to-morrow.

"We are going to Yorkshire to-morrow and we will come back next year," I said at last. "Will you meet us at the Spring Fair?"

"I will meet you at Devizes Spring Fair if I have to travel a hundred miles to get there. Give me both yer hands, my brothers. Tell me, have you made up yer mind to go to Yorkshire?"

"Yes."

"Then I cannot find it in my heart to let you go without any money." He pulled a shilling out of his pocket. " Look

286

at this shilling," he said, holding it up to the light. " If that was the last piece of silver I had in the world I would give you, God Almighty strike me stone blind, sixpence of it! Now while there is no one else here I am a-going to lend you enough money to start off on the roads. I couldn't see you or any other traveller go with nothing in their pockets. Georgina, give them four pound-notes."

The woman drew a wad of notes from her breast. She picked out the required number, and after a long argument we stowed them away in our wallets.

The sun set, and as the twilight faded the shadows cast by the light of the fire grew stronger and bolder. In the other camps the various families were sitting round their fires eating their evening meal. The peace of night-fall descended on the lane. A low rumble of voices came from the fires, a cry of a child, the whine of a dog, the jingle of crocks. In the hedge a blackbird suddenly burst into a brief vigorous song before it settled down for the night. A cold breeze, which reminded me that it was still early spring, stirred, blowing the smoke into my eyes, and I moved round and sat under the hedge. I looked at the countless half-open leaves in the hedge and the fresh green shoots of grass, and remembered the boy's remark about his sister, " One day their clothes hang on 'em, and the next day they seems to be a-bursting out of 'em."

I looked across the fire at Miranda. She was sitting on the grass opposite me, her head was on one side, she was looking into the fire, and I could just catch a glimpse of the deep red light reflected in her eyes. Arthur was telling Christopher that he would be glad to get up on the wide grass Ridgeway which runs along the edge of the downs from Swindon to Wantage. Bare, open chalk downs. Hawthorn and blackthorn hedges, wheat fields, sheep, dog-roses, cowslips, plover. I imagined Miranda all the summer wandering passively along the ridge of these hills, sleeping on the rough ground, eating under hedges, gathering wild flowers and selling them in the villages and towns.

In spite of the opening leaves and the springing grass, none of the travellers had recognized the arrival of spring until the Fair was over. Two days before they had talked of the weather and their movements in terms of winter, but now the Spring Fair was over and the summer had, for them, instantly begun. Two days before, it seemed that they would have been content to remain in the lane for months, now they all seemed restless and anxious to be on the move.

Since I had been travelling with horses I looked upon distance as it was looked upon by people two centuries ago. I was no longer surprised at hearing three hundred miles spoken of as a month's journey, and Yorkshire was to me, as to every Gypsy man, woman, and child in Wiltshire, the *waver tem*—the other country.